STEYR RAUPENSCHLEPPER OST (GERMAN)

FIAT TM40 TRATTORE MEDIO (ITALIAN)

FORD HEAVY UTILITY CAR (BRITISH)

VICTOR
BOOK FOR BOYS 1977

CONTENTS

Printed and Published in Great Britain by D. C. THOMSON & CO., LTD., 185 Fleet Street, London, EC4A 2HS.

BATTLE FOR MALTA

On June 11th, 1940, Italy entered World War Two. At that time, the total air defence of the Mediterranean island fortress of Malta consisted of three obsolete Gloster Gladiator biplane fighters. These were nicknamed Faith, Hope and Charity.

5

Only a month before, in May, 1940, the island had no fighter defence, but three Gloster Gladiators were borrowed from the Navy . . .

RIGHT, YOU LOT. GET THOSE PACKING CASES OPENED. WE'VE HAD TO MOVE HEAVEN AND EARTH TO GET HOLD OF THESE THREE FIGHTERS.

WELL, THAT'S THIS ONE ALMOST COMPLETE BUT I WOULDN'T LIKE TO TAKE ON THE EYETIES IN ONE OF THESE OLD CRATES.

The day Italy entered the war, the first wave of Italian bombers appeared over the island.

THE EYETIES ARE OUT TO BOMB GRAND HARBOUR. LET'S GET AT 'EM!

GOT HIM! THAT'S ONE THAT WON'T BE GOING HOME TONIGHT!

Some weeks later, a few Hurricane fighters reached the island and they, with the Gladiators, kept the Italians and their German allies at bay.

Early in 1942, Spitfires were flown from the American aircraft carrier 'Wasp' to the island, but the Germans caught them on the ground just after they landed and very few survived.

Then, early in May, 1942 . . .

THE AIRCRAFT CARRIERS 'EAGLE' AND 'WASP' ARE ON THEIR WAY. BETWEEN THEM, THEY ARE CARRYING SIXTY-FOUR SPITFIRES FOR US. THESE PLANES WILL BE FLOWN OFF EARLY IN THE MORNING OF MAY 9TH.

BUT, SIR, WON'T THE JERRIES CATCH THEM ON THE GROUND AGAIN?

Early on the morning of the ninth . . .

NO, THEY WON'T! THESE PLANES WILL LAND, BE REFUELLED, ARMED AND IN THE AIR AGAIN WITH A MALTA PILOT AT THE CONTROLS WITHIN MINUTES! OR I'LL WANT TO KNOW WHY NOT!

MALTA, HERE WE COME!

SPITFIRES! HEADING FOR MALTA. GET THE BOMBERS IN THE AIR!

ACH, THESE BRITISHERS WILL NEVER LEARN. WE WILL BOMB THESE SPITFIRES ON THE GROUND LIKE WE DID LAST TIME.

Meanwhile . . .

HERE COME THE SPITFIRES, LADS! NOW OUR WORK REALLY STARTS!

RIGHT, MATE. OVER HERE TO THE DISPERSAL POINT—QUICK AS YOU CAN!

8

THE TOUGH OF THE TRACK

Alf Tupper, the runner known as the Tough of the Track, lived and worked in Greystone. Alf was one of the country's top middle-distance runners and was now taking part in a sports meeting celebrating the founding of Greystone 500 years before. In the last lap of the 1500 metres race, Alf pulled out to overtake Rupert Snyke, another local runner . . .

SNYKE'S SLOWING UP A BIT! NOW'S MY CHANCE!

I'M NOT LETTING THAT ROUGHNECK TUPPER PAST!

THAT'LL TAKE THE WIND OUT OF HIS SAILS.

OOOF!

THE RACE IS MINE NOW! AFTER THAT, TUPPER WON'T MANAGE TO RAISE ANOTHER SPRINT.

But Alf wasn't called the Tough of the Track for nothing . . .

I'LL SORT HIM OUT ABOUT THAT AFTER THE RACE. BUT NOW I'VE GOT TO WIN IT.

TUPPER! BUT HOW...

10

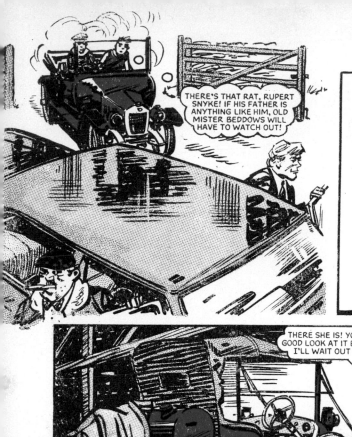

THERE'S THAT RAT, RUPERT SNYKE! IF HIS FATHER IS ANYTHING LIKE HIM, OLD MISTER BEDDOWS WILL HAVE TO WATCH OUT!

I PRESUME YOU GENTLEMEN ARE HERE ABOUT THE PRIORMOBILE. WELL, SHE'S IN THE OLD BARN OVER THERE. COME AND HAVE A LOOK.

THERE SHE IS! YOU CAN HAVE A GOOD LOOK AT IT BY YOURSELVES. I'LL WAIT OUT IN THE YARD.

WHAT ARE YOU DOING HERE, GUTTERSNIPE? YOU HAVEN'T THE MONEY TO BUY A CAR LIKE THIS!

I'M HERE WITH MISTER BEDDOWS AND I'M GOING TO MAKE SURE YOU DON'T TRY ANY DIRTY TRICKS LIKE YOU DID ON THE RUNNING TRACK!

YES, THIS CAR IS IN EXCELLENT CONDITION. I'LL BUY IT AND WHEN I DIE IT CAN BE PASSED ON WITH MY OTHER CAR TO THE CITY MUSEUM.

YES, I'LL HAVE THIS. IN A FEW YEARS, IT'LL BE WORTH A LOT MORE AND I CAN MAKE A GOOD TAX-FREE KILLING ON IT.

WELL, YOU'VE BOTH SEEN THE CAR AND YOU KNOW WHAT IT'S LIKE. MY PRICE, AND I'M NOT GOING TO HAGGLE, IS TWO AND A HALF THOUSAND.

I'LL BUY IT.

DONE! I'LL TAKE IT.

THAT'S BEDDOWS' LIMIT! I'LL GIVE YOU ANOTHER FIVE HUNDRED.

NO, THAT'S NOT MY WAY. I'VE SET MY PRICE AND THAT'S WHAT I WANT. WE'LL HAVE TO SETTLE THIS ANOTHER WAY.

IT'S AGAINST CLUB RULES BUT I'LL TELL YOU WHAT I'LL DO. I'LL SELL THE CAR, AT MY STATED PRICE, TO THE ONE WITH THE BEST TIME IN THE MEETING ON SATURDAY. YOU'VE BOTH GOT VINTAGE CARS ALREADY AND THEY'RE WELL MATCHED. SO IT'LL BE A FAIR CONTEST.

As well as the athletic race around the city boundaries on the following Saturday, there was to be a meeting for vintage cars. They were to follow the same route as the runners but were to leave later so that everyone should finish about the same time.

WELL, HOW ABOUT IT?

YES, THAT'S FAIR ENOUGH BY ME.

IF THAT'S HOW YOU WANT IT. BUT YOU'D BE BETTER TAKING MY MONEY AND BEING OVER AND DONE WITH IT.

I DON'T TRUST THOSE TWO. THEY'LL BE UP TO SOMETHING.

IT'S AS GOOD AS MINE. I'LL MAKE SURE THAT OLD FOOL, BEDDOWS, DOESN'T EVEN FINISH ON SATURDAY!

On the Friday, Alf went for a training run along the streets, in a quiet part of Greystone . . .

IT'S UP NEAR HERE THAT OLD MISTER BEDDOWS LIVES. I HOPE HE MANAGES TO BEAT THAT SNAKE, SNYKE, TOMORROW.

BLIMEY! SNYKE! WHAT ARE YOU DOING HERE, PIE-FACE?

NOT THAT IT'S ANY OF YOUR BUSINESS, GUTTERSNIPE, BUT I'M GOING OUT FOR A TRAINING RUN. MUST KEEP FIT TO THRASH YOU TOMORROW.

THERE'S A FEW OF THE BLOKES TRAIN ROUND HERE BECAUSE IT'S SO QUIET— BUT THAT'S THE FIRST TIME I'VE SEEN HIM!

Next day, Alf lined up for the start of the race round the boundaries . . .

NO USE IN HANGING ABOUT AND GETTING BUNCHED IN. I'LL GET INTO THE LEAD QUICKLY.

NOW TO GET IN FRONT!

MADE IT! NOW I CAN SETTLE DOWN A BIT. THERE'S A LONG WAY TO GO.

Alf was still in front with three miles to go . . .

THERE GOES MISTER BEDDOWS! HE'S IN FRONT OF OLD SNYKE.

THERE'S SNYKE NOW! BUT WHY'S HE LOOKING SO HAPPY? HE'S GOING TO LOSE.

But a little further on . . .

HARD LUCK, MISTER BEDDOWS! WHAT'S HAPPENED?

IT'S THE PROP SHAFT AGAIN, ALF. IT'S EXACTLY THE SAME NOISE.

NO, IT CAN'T BE! I FIXED THAT RIGHT. IT WOULDN'T SLACKEN OFF AGAIN SO QUICKLY.

IT IS LOOSE! HOW— RUPERT SNYKE! THAT'S WHAT HE WAS DOING UP NEAR MISTER BEDDOWS' HOUSE. THE LOUSY RAT!

THAT'S IT FIXED AND THERE GOES THAT RAT, SNYKE.

YOU GET AFTER OLD SNYKE IN HIS CAR. I'M GOING TO BEAT HIS SON!

THOSE SNYKES ARE AS LOW AS THEY COME. THEY AIN'T GOING TO WIN ANYTHING IF I CAN HELP IT.

OH, NO, HERE COMES BEDDOWS. HOW DID HE GET GOING AGAIN? I'D BETTER SPEED UP!

15

The End

THE STRANGLEHOLD FROM FORTY FATHOMS

The giant nuclear bomber, Able Four, of the U.S. Strategic Air Command, was flying at eighty thousand feet above the Atlantic on the last leg of its long patrol—and the crew was happy to be going home.

U.S. AIR FORCE

OUR ESTIMATED TIME OF ARRIVAL IS SIX-TWENTY, SKIP.

GREAT STUFF, HANK. WE'LL BE IN PLENTY OF TIME TO CATCH THE BALL GAME.

But metal fatigue fractured a small rivet in the starboard wing and sealed the fate of Able Four and its crew.

USAF

GREAT BALLS OF FIRE! WHAT'S HAPPENING?

THE STARBOARD WING'S BREAKING UP!

MAYDAY! MAYDAY! ABLE FOUR TO BASE...

The stricken bomber plunged into the Sargasso Sea.

After many months the plane was still not found and the search was abandoned. Over the years, the casings of the nuclear bombs gradually cracked under the tremendous pressure and the escaping radiation had a peculiar effect on a certain type of seaweed.

17

Seventy years later, in 2046, the merchant hovercraft Whisperer was making its way from Rio de Janeiro to London. On board were Captain Bill Henderson, radio-operator and navigator Geoff Evans, and engineer Binky Dobbs.

HEY, SKIPPER, THERE'S A NEWS-FLASH COMING THROUGH.

THE TRANSATLANTIC HYDROFOIL, MARINA, HAS DISAPPEARED WITHOUT TRACE EN ROUTE FOR NEW YORK. ALL VESSELS ARE REQUESTED TO KEEP A LOOK-OUT FOR ANY SIGNS OF HER.

HMM. THOSE HYDROFOILS CAN TRAVEL AT OVER 200 MILES AN HOUR. SOMETHING MUST HAVE GONE WRONG. WELL, WE'LL KEEP A SHARP LOOK-OUT WHEN WE REACH THE SEARCH AREA.

Early next morning.

HEY, BILL, ISN'T THAT THE MISSING HYDROFOIL?

YEAH, IT'S THE MARINA, ALL RIGHT. SHE'S 700 MILES OFF COURSE. I WONDER WHAT'S WRONG? WE'LL STEER FOR HER.

I CAN'T RAISE HER ON THE RADIO, BILL. HER SET MUST BE DEAD!

SHE'S RAISING SIGNAL FLAGS—"URGENT ASSISTANCE NEEDED. COME ALONGSIDE!"

RIGHT, LET'S SEE—HEY, WHAT'S GOING ON?

IT'S THE MARINA'S MECHANICAL GRABS—THEY'VE GOT HOLD OF US!

THEY'RE LIFTING US ABOARD. AND THEY'RE MOVING OFF TOO! THERE'S SOMETHING VERY FISHY GOING ON HERE!

18

WHAT'S THE MEANING OF THIS? I DEMAND TO SEE THE CAPTAIN IMMEDIATELY!

AND SO YOU SHALL, MATEY. TAKE THEM AWAY!

IN THERE! THAT'S WHERE CAPTAIN HARDACRE IS. HEH-HEH!

WHAT'S GOING ON? WHAT HAPPENED TO THE CAPTAIN?

PIRACY—THAT'S WHAT'S GOING ON. WE WERE TWO DAYS OUT OF LIVERPOOL WHEN THE CREW TOOK OVER. THEY'RE AFTER THE GOLD BULLION WE'RE CARRYING IN OUR STRONG-ROOM—FIFTEEN MILLION POUNDS WORTH! CAPTAIN HARDACRE WAS HIT OVER THE HEAD WHEN HE TRIED TO RESIST!

I'M FEELING BETTER NOW. TAGGART, WHO'S IN CHARGE OF THESE CUT-THROATS, TOLD ME THEY WERE HEADING FOR THE SARGASSO SEA WHERE THEY'RE GOING TO BREAK IN TO THE STRONG-ROOM AND TRANSFER THE GOLD TO A HIGH-POWERED LAUNCH, THE GREY FALCON.

I SUPPOSE THEY KIDNAPPED US SO THAT WE COULDN'T GIVE AWAY THEIR POSITION TO THE SEARCH PARTY.

HEY—WE'VE STOPPED! WE MUST BE IN THE SARGASSO SEA.

RIGHT, YOU LOT—OUTSIDE! TAGGART WANTS TO SEE YOU.

COME IN, GENTLEMEN. IT WAS NICE OF YOU TO DROP IN ON US. WE'RE ABOUT TO START ON THE STRONG-ROOM AND WE WANT YOU LOT TOGETHER TO KEEP AN EYE ON YOU.

YOU'LL BE SORRY FOR THIS, TAGGART. THIS IS PIRACY AND KIDNAPPING.

YOU MUST BE THE NAVIGATION OFFICER. WHERE ARE WE?

FIVE MILES INSIDE THE SARGASSO SEA. AND I'M NOT SO SURE WE'LL GET OUT AGAIN. THERE'S SOMETHING FUNNY ABOUT THE SEAWEED—IT'S CLOSING IN ON US. I'VE NEVER SEEN ANYTHING LIKE IT BEFORE!

Two hours later.

RIGHT, WE'VE GOT INTO THE STRONG-ROOM AND WE'LL PILE THE BULLION IN HERE FOR NOW. JONESY, YOU SIGNAL THE GREY FALCON TO COME IN AND WE'LL TRANSFER THE GOLD TO HER.

RIGHT, BUTCH!

19

Minutes later.

BUTCH, THE FALCON SAYS SHE CAN'T COME IN BECAUSE THE WEED IS TOO THICK. AND THERE'S SOMETHING ELSE—JIM AND NOBBY WERE ON GUARD UP ON DECK AND THEY'VE DISAPPEARED!

DISAPPEARED? HUH, THEY'LL BE DODGING OFF SOMEWHERE! BUT IF FALCON CAN'T COME IN WE'LL HAVE TO GO OUT. YOU TWO START LUGGING THESE BOXES UP TO THE DECK!

PHEW! THIS GOLD AIN'T HALF HEAVY!

QUIT YACKING AND GET A MOVE ON!

LOOK! LOOK AT THE SEAWEED!

I'LL SOON SHIFT IT!

HELP! IT'S GOT ME!

HOLD ON!

BILL! IT'S GOT ME TOO!

AAGH!

I'M COMING, BINKY!

HURRY, BILL, HURRY!

Suddenly the hydrofoil shuddered.

Shortly, aboard the Whisperer.

21

22

IT WORKED A TREAT! I'LL TIE UP THESE TWO AND HEAD BACK TO THE MARINA.

Bill radioed the U.S. Coastguard and headed back to the Marina.

WOW! THERE'S EVEN MORE SEAWEED ON IT. THEY CAN'T LAST MUCH LONGER!

AHOY, MARINA! TAGGART AND HIS MATE ARE MY PRISONERS NOW. SURRENDER TO THE CAPTAIN AND HIS OFFICERS AND I'LL TRY TO GET YOU OUT OF THERE.

AH, THEY'RE SIGNALLING THAT THE ORIGINAL CREW ARE IN CHARGE. NOW LET'S SEE IF I CAN GET THEM OUT OF THERE. I'M TAKING A HECK OF A GAMBLE, BUT I THINK THE HEAT FROM THE WHISPERER'S ENGINES SHOULD BE STRONG ENOUGH IF I TURN THEM UP TO FULL POWER.

IT'S WORKING! IT'S BURNING THE WEED!

WHISPERER

IF I BURN A PATH THROUGH THE WEED, THE MARINA CAN FOLLOW ME OUT.

Later, aboard a U.S. Coastguard ship.

WELL, THANKS TO YOU, WE'VE ROUNDED UP THE WHOLE GANG, INCLUDING THE CREW OF THE GREY FALCON. THEY'LL ALL SPEND A LONG TIME BEHIND BARS.

THINK NOTHING OF IT, CAPTAIN. IT LIVENED UP WHAT WOULD HAVE BEEN A VERY BORING JOURNEY.

A REGIMENT OF FOREIGNERS

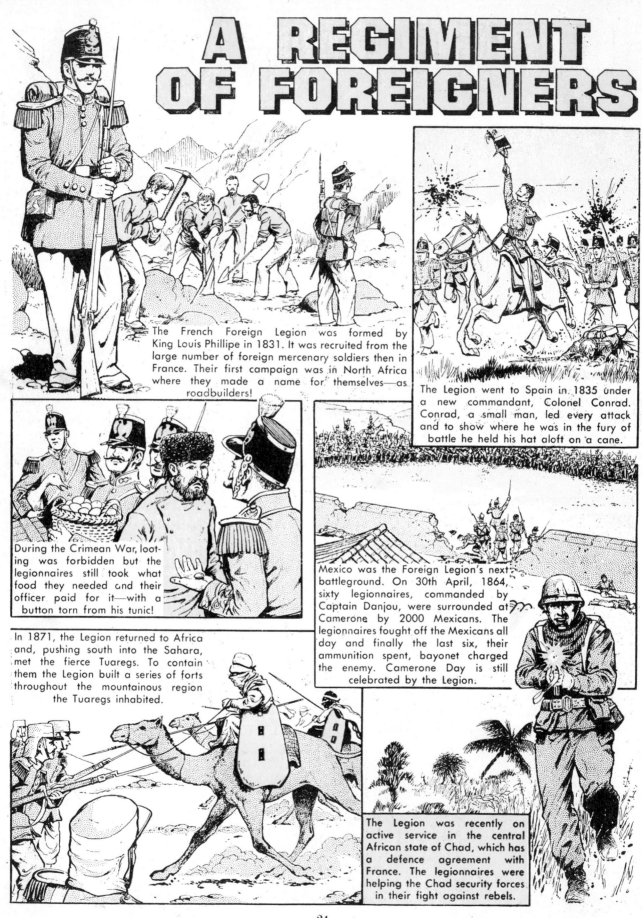

The French Foreign Legion was formed by King Louis Phillipe in 1831. It was recruited from the large number of foreign mercenary soldiers then in France. Their first campaign was in North Africa where they made a name for themselves—as roadbuilders!

The Legion went to Spain in 1835 under a new commandant, Colonel Conrad. Conrad, a small man, led every attack and to show where he was in the fury of battle he held his hat aloft on a cane.

During the Crimean War, looting was forbidden but the legionnaires still took what food they needed and their officer paid for it—with a button torn from his tunic!

In 1871, the Legion returned to Africa and, pushing south into the Sahara, met the fierce Tuaregs. To contain them the Legion built a series of forts throughout the mountainous region the Tuaregs inhabited.

Mexico was the Foreign Legion's next battleground. On 30th April, 1864, sixty legionnaires, commanded by Captain Danjou, were surrounded at Camerone by 2000 Mexicans. The legionnaires fought off the Mexicans all day and finally the last six, their ammunition spent, bayonet charged the enemy. Camerone Day is still celebrated by the Legion.

The Legion was recently on active service in the central African state of Chad, which has a defence agreement with France. The legionnaires were helping the Chad security forces in their fight against rebels.

24

LOCKE OF THE LEGION

In 1925 the desert tribes of Syria rose in revolt against the French and the Foreign Legion was sent to quell the uprising. Split into small groups, the legionnaires were sent to reinforce the native police. Two Englishmen, Tom Locke and Bill Sommerfield, were in the detachment sent to El Al, in the foothills of the interior, and they were now marching into the town square. Bill was a new recruit but Tom had been in the Legion for five years.

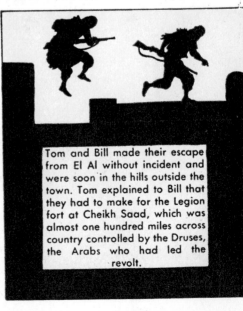

Tom and Bill made their escape from El Al without incident and were soon in the hills outside the town. Tom explained to Bill that they had to make for the Legion fort at Cheikh Saad, which was almost one hundred miles across country controlled by the Druses, the Arabs who had led the revolt.

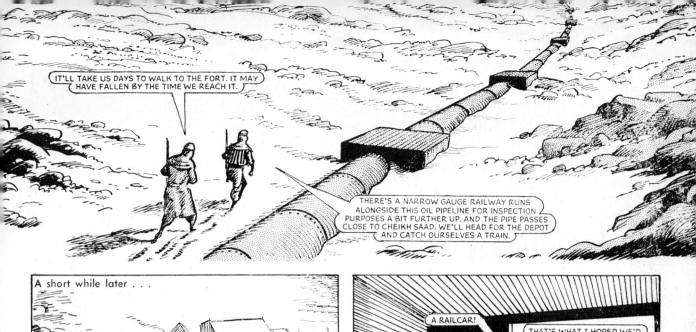

27

LOOK AT THIS RIFLE, TOM. I TOOK IT FROM ONE OF THE DEAD DRUSES. IT'S NEW AND GERMAN MADE—BETTER THAN OUR RIFLES.

NEW GRENADES TOO. BUT WE'VE GOT OTHER THINGS TO THINK ABOUT JUST NOW. FOR A DYING MAN THAT DRUSE SPOKE PLENTY.

Tom and Bill selected the best of the captured camels and set off in a bid to reach the fort at Cheikh Saad before the Druses arrived. They rode all night, but as dawn streaked the sky they heard the sound of small-arms fire which told them that the Druses had already laid seige to the fort.

TWENTY-SEVEN WAR BANNERS. THERE ARE PROBABLY NEARER SIX THOUSAND THAN FIVE THOUSAND MEN. BUT THERE'S SOMETHING ODD ABOUT THIS SET-UP.

THE NORMAL DRUSE TACTIC IS TO RUSH THE ENEMY IN A FRONTAL ATTACK BUT THIS LOT SEEM TO BE WAITING FOR SOMETHING TO HAPPEN. I'M GOING DOWN THERE TO FIND OUT WHAT'S GOING ON. YOU STAY HERE AND KEEP OUT OF SIGHT, BILL.

OKAY, TOM. I'VE GOT A FEELING MY RIG-OUT WOULDN'T FOOL A GENUINE ARAB.

I HOPE HE GETS BACK ALL RIGHT. I WOULDN'T GIVE MUCH FOR MY CHANCES WITHOUT HIS EXPERIENCE TO GUIDE ME.

Bill continued to watch until Locke was out of sight, when suddenly . . .

DO NOT MOVE FOR YOUR RIFLE—YOU WILL BE DEAD BEFORE YOU REACH IT.

29

THE HAIRCUT OF A LEGIONNAIRE. KILL HIM!

NO, NOT YET. WE WILL FIRST TAKE HIM TO THE EMIR.

HERR VON SCHNEK, THIS IS A LEGIONNAIRE DISGUISED AS AN ARAB. HE MUST HAVE ESCAPED FROM THE FORT.

WERE YOU SENT TO GET HELP? WERE YOU GIVEN A LETTER? SO YOU CHOOSE NOT TO REPLY—VERY WELL. SEARCH HIM!

HIGHNESS, WE HAVE CAUGHT AND SHOT A LEGIONNAIRE DISGUISED AS ONE OF US.

THEY MUST HAVE CAUGHT TOM!

ANOTHER LEGIONNAIRE IN DISGUISE! THE LONGER WE DELAY ATTACKING THE GREATER THE RISK OF ONE OF THEM GETTING THROUGH AND BRINGING REINFORCEMENTS. I SAY WE SHOULD ATTACK NOW.

PATIENCE, EMIR. THE MORTARS WILL ARRIVE IN A FEW HOURS AND AFTER THEY HAVE DESTROYED THE WALLS YOU WILL BE ABLE TO STORM THE FORT EASILY. BUT WHAT WILL YOU DO WITH THIS PRISONER?

HE WILL BE STAKED OUT IN THE DESERT AND LEFT FOR THE SUN TO BURN AND THE JACKALS TO EAT. HIS DEATH WILL BE A WARNING TO OTHERS.

STRUGGLE, LEGION DOG, BUT YOU WON'T ESCAPE. SOON THE JACKALS WILL COME AND EAT YOU.

That night . . .

THAT NOISE—IT MUST BE A JACKAL! GET AWAY, JACKAL! BEAT IT! SCRAM!

THAT'S NO WAY TO TALK TO YOUR RESCUER, BILL.

I THOUGHT THEY'D GOT YOU, TOM.

THEY DID GET A LEGIONNAIRE BUT IT WASN'T ME—I'M TOO WILY. NOW LET'S GET DOWN TO THE BRIDGE ACROSS THE WADI AND I'LL TELL YOU WHAT I'VE FOUND OUT.

VON SCHNECK IS A KEY MAN IN A BIG GERMAN ARMAMENTS FIRM WHICH IS SECRETLY SUPPLYING THE REBELS WITH ARMS. THE FIRM ALSO OWNS THE PIPELINE AND IS SMUGGLING THE ARMS IN IN CASES MARKED 'MACHINERY'.

VON SCHNECK PROMISED MORTARS. I HEARD HIM AND THE EMIR TALKING ABOUT THEM.

THEY'VE ARRIVED AND THEY'RE SET UP IN THE WADI READY TO OPEN UP AT FIRST LIGHT. THE GARRISON DOESN'T STAND A CHANCE—UNLESS WE CAN DO SOMETHING.

SUCH AS? AND ANYWAY, WHY ARE THEY CONCENTRATING SO MUCH ON THIS FORT?

FORT CHEIKH SAAD COMMANDS AN IMPORTANT PASS FROM THE HINTERLAND TO THE COAST. WITH FREE ACCESS TO THE SEA THE DRUSES CAN GET ALL THE ARMS THEY CAN PAY FOR, WHICH MEANS BIG PROFITS FOR VON SCHNECK. BUT WE'RE GOING TO THROW A SPANNER IN THE WORKS.

WE'LL BLOW UP THE OIL PIPE WHERE IT CROSSES THE WADI. THE WADI WILL BECOME A RIVER OF FIRE AND THE DRUSES WILL RUN FOR THEIR CAMELS AND AWAY FROM THE FORT. THE LEGION WON'T BE ABLE TO FOLLOW UP ACROSS THE WADI BUT WE'LL BE ON THE RIGHT SIDE TO CAPTURE VON SCHNEK AND SMASH HIS ARMS RACKET.

Locke ran on to the bridge and planted two grenades against the pipe. He then pulled the ring on the third before laying it beside the other two.

YOU'VE DONE IT, TOM. WELL DONE!

THE END

THE MASTS OF MENACE

JERRY'S FOUND US AGAIN. HE ALWAYS SEEMS TO KNOW EXACTLY WHERE WE ARE! TAKE THAT, YOU HUN!

In the spring of 1943, during World War Two, British convoys of vital supplies stood between the hard-pressed Russian Army and defeat. The Germans tried everything in their power to stop the ships getting through.

At the War Office, the Germans' success at finding the convoys had not gone unnoticed.

ACTING ON INFORMATION RECEIVED FROM ONE OF OUR AGENTS, NILS YONGSTROM, WE'VE PHOTOGRAPHED THIS AREA HERE IN NORTHERN NORWAY AND FOUND A NEW GERMAN RADIO LOCATION CENTRE. IT IS FROM HERE THAT OUR CONVOYS ARE BEING PLOTTED. WE INTEND TO WIPE IT OUT!

BUT HOW? THAT'S PRETTY RUGGED COUNTRY AROUND THERE. IT WON'T BE AN EASY TARGET TO ATTACK.

WE'RE GOING TO LAND A GLIDER FULL OF CRACK TROOPS NEAR THE STATION. THEY'LL WIPE IT OUT AND THEN MAKE THEIR WAY TO THE COAST WHERE WE HOPE THE NAVY WILL PICK THEM UP!

DON'T WORRY ABOUT THAT. YOU TELL ME WHEN, AND THERE'LL BE A SUBMARINE WAITING FOR THEM.

And so, a few nights later, a glider carrying a troop of tough, hard-hitting commandos took off for Norway.

But, over the Norwegian coast . . .

A JERRY FIGHTER—AND IT'S HIT US!

33

But the snow wasn't as flat and level as it seemed . . .

THAT CAVE'LL DO. WHAT A STROKE OF LUCK!

In the cave, Joe fell asleep. Then, suddenly, he wakened . . .

EH? WHAT?.

DO NOT WORRY! I AM OF THE RESISTANCE. WE HAVE HAD MEN SEARCHING FOR YOU ALL DAY. LUCKILY, I SAW THE TRACKS LEADING TO THIS CAVE BEFORE THE GERMANS DID.

GOOD! I WAS HOPING TO MEET UP WITH YOU LOT. I MUST GET IN TOUCH WITH NILS YONGSTROM.

THAT IS NO BOTHER! HE IS MY SON! HE HELPS ME ON OUR FARM.

THAT'S A PIECE OF LUCK! LET'S GO AND SEE HIM.

Later . . .

THERE IS THE FARM. NILS WILL BE THERE. ONE OF US ALWAYS STAYS IN CASE ANY GERMANS PAY US A VISIT.

THAT'S A GOOD NOTION. YOU CAN'T BE TOO CAREFUL.

THIS IS JOE FRANKLIN, NILS. HE IS THE ONLY SURVIVOR OF THE COMMANDOS.

IT IS A TRAGEDY. NOW WE WILL NOT BE ABLE TO BLOW UP THE RADIO STATION.

DON'T BE TOO SURE OF THAT! JUST YOU TELL ME WHAT YOU CAN ABOUT THE STATION AND WE'LL SEE WHAT CAN BE DONE.

THERE IS A DOUBLE FENCE ROUND THE PERIMETER WITH GUARDS AT BOTH GATES. THE RADIO EQUIPMENT IS ON THE LEFT, INSIDE THE INNER GATE.

HOW DO YOU KNOW SO MUCH ABOUT IT? YOU SEEM TO KNOW THE LAYOUT LIKE THE BACK OF YOUR HAND.

I DELIVER BUTTER AND EGGS THERE EVERY DAY. I STARTED DOING IT AS A WAY TO KEEP A CLOSE EYE ON THE GERMANS.

A GOOD IDEA! BUT IT'S MORE THAN THAT. IT'S MY WAY TO GET INSIDE. I'LL GO INSTEAD OF YOU TOMORROW.

CAN YOU SKI? NILS ALWAYS GOES ON HIS SKIS.

YES, I CAN SKI. I DID SOME BEFORE THE WAR AND I'VE BEEN ON A COUPLE OF COURSES WITH THE COMMANDOS.

GOOD! YOU WEAR MY SKI SUIT. THE GERMANS WON'T SUSPECT ANYTHING. THEY ARE USED TO SEEING ME COMING EVERY DAY.

Next afternoon, Joe set out on his dangerous mission.

WE'LL WAIT HERE, JOE, TO GIVE YOU COVERING FIRE WHEN YOU MAKE YOUR ESCAPE! GOOD LUCK!

KEEP YOUR FINGERS ON THE TRIGGER. THE JERRIES WILL BE AFTER ME LIKE A PACK OF HOUNDS WHEN I COME OUT OF THERE.

YOU HAVE BROUGHT THE BUTTER AND EGGS, JA? TAKE THEM TO THE COOKHOUSE AS USUAL!

SO FAR—SO GOOD.

THE CONCRETE BUILDING TO THE LEFT OF THE GATE—THAT'S WHAT NILS SAID.

YOU ARE NOT ALLOWED NEAR HERE! AAH!

SORRY, NO TIME TO EXPLAIN.

36

GORGEOUS GUS

The Earl of Boote, nicknamed Gorgeous Gus, was the owner and captain of Redburn Rovers. Now, in the last game of the season, Rovers had to beat Blackport United to become First Division Champions . . .

The match took place next day. Before the game began, in Moravia's beautiful stadium, both teams were presented to King Frederik.

Shortly after, Gus scored another to make it 3-1 for the Rovers.

Gus received permission from the referee to leave the field.

Ten minutes later, Moravia Dynamo scored . . .

Just before the full-time whistle . . .

Each team had to take five penalty kicks, and the score stood at 5-4 to Moravia Dynamo as Gus strode up to take Rovers' last kick . . .

The End

47

A QUESTION OF FOOTBALL

ANSWERS ON PAGE 80

1—Can a ball be passed to another player from a penalty kick?

YES

2—Who was the first professional footballer to be knighted?

S. MATHEWS

3—Where were the last five World Cup finals played?

GERMANY, BRAZIL

4—It is well known that Scotland play most of their international matches at Hampden Park, Glasgow, but which famous Scottish amateur team plays there, and what is its nickname?

QUEENS PARK

HARTLEPOOL

5—A goalkeeper takes a goal-kick and accidentally pushes the ball into his net after the ball has been blown back from outside the penalty area by the wind. Is it a goal?

YES

6—The four animals above represent the nicknames of four English soccer teams. Who are they?

7—Which European club had, at one time, three European Footballers of the Year playing for them?

MAN UTD

ANSWERS TO "QUICK QUIZ"

1 The doctor in London was his sister.

2 Victor.

3 Never! The ship rises with the tide.

4 Italy; France; Wales; Israel.

5 HEAD HEAD   TAIL HEAD

6 He crossed with the goose, returned, and crossed with the fox. Took the goose back, left it, and took the corn over. He then went back for the goose.

7

THE FINGER OF DEATH

In March, 1944, during the Second World War, the Allied advance had ground to a halt on the Mareno Plain in Italy. The Germans had placed concealed artillery on the hills commanding the plain, and artillery observers on a pinnacle of rock known as the Malveni Finger, ten miles inside their lines. The observers, from their commanding position, were able to report any movement on the plain to the gunners—and the gunners did the rest.

WELL, WE'RE THE ONLY TWO LEFT NOW, SIR. SHALL WE STILL KEEP ON ADVANCING?

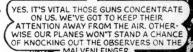

YES. IT'S VITAL THOSE GUNS CONCENTRATE ON US. WE'VE GOT TO KEEP THEIR ATTENTION AWAY FROM THE AIR. OTHERWISE OUR PLANES WON'T STAND A CHANCE OF KNOCKING OUT THE OBSERVERS ON THE MALVENI FINGER.

THERE'S THE FINGER—DEAD AHEAD! THOSE TANK BOYS ARE BEING SLAUGHTERED DOWN THERE, BUYING TIME FOR US. LET'S SHOW THEM WE APPRECIATE IT.

THE WHOLE GROUND'S ALIVE WITH ACK-ACK. THEY MUST HAVE EXPECTED AN ATTACK LIKE THIS! WE'RE TAKING A HAMMERING!

But the observation post was not on top of the Malveni Finger . . .

Meanwhile, back in England, Private Joe Bones had his own problems. Joe was a terrible soldier but a great climber, which often landed him in all sorts of hot water. Now he was talking to Lord Plimpton from the War Office . . .

LORD PLIMPTON—LOOK AT ME! I CAN'T WEAR THIS! I LOOK LIKE SOMETHING OUT OF A HORROR MOVIE! AND AS FOR CLIMBING IN IT—BLIMEY!

THAT'S THE END OF THEM, SIR. SIX PLANES LOST, A WHOLE SECTION OF TANKS DESTROYED—AND ALL WE'VE SUFFERED IS A BIT OF A HEADACHE WHEN THE BOMB WENT OFF ABOVE US. THEY CAN'T TOUCH US HERE.

THE ACK-ACK AND THE OVERHANG GUARD US FROM THE AIR—AND THE SENTRIES ON THE STEPS PROTECT US FROM BELOW. ONLY THE SHEER DROP IS UNGUARDED—BUT THE BRITISH WOULD NEED A SUPERMAN TO GET UP THAT!

DO CHEER UP, OLD FELLOW. IT'S NOT EVERYBODY THAT HAS THE HONOUR OF FIRST TRYING OUT PROFESSOR HANNIGAN'S SUCTION CLIMBERS! BONES, THESE COULD REVOLUTIONISE WARFARE. IMAGINE IT, WITH THESE ON HIS HANDS AND FEET, EVEN A CHILD COULD CLIMB UP A SHEER CLIFF FACE!

HOW CAN I TRUST MYSELF TO THIS LOT? IT'S OBVIOUSLY GOIN' TO BLOW UP AT ANY MINUTE. I TELL YOU, GUV, IF I TRY AND CLIMB LIKE THIS, I'LL BREAK ME NECK!

DO STOP WHINING, BONES. I HAVE PERFECT FAITH IN THE PROFESSOR'S INVENTION, AND SO SHOULD YOU. AH—HERE COMES THE GENIUS NOW!

AH, PRIVATE BONES—ALL READY FOR THE DEMONSTRATION? JUST REMEMBER, THE CUPS WILL GRIP THE ROCK LIKE GLUE, AND THAT THE ONLY WAY OF BREAKING THAT HOLD IS TO TURN THEM IN A CLOCKWISE DIRECTION. UP YOU GO!

BUT, PROFESSOR, COULDN'T I—

BONES—UP!

50

But nobody heard . . .

Eventually Joe managed to prise the suckers loose. He then completed the climb and made his way back to the camp . . .

And, in spite of Joe's protest, within two days . . .

The invention worked silently and well for the first fifty feet. Then . . .

LOOK OUT! WE'RE BEING ATTACKED!

OH, NO—THAT'S TORN IT! WELL, 'ERE GOES!

BLIMEY—I GOT THE LOT! I DON'T BELIEVE IT. NORMALLY I 'AVE TO USE A FULL MAGAZINE TO 'IT JUST ONE BLOKE!

Joe quickly got the rope ladder out of his rucksack and lowered it to the ground. And shortly . . .

'ULLO, GUV— ENJOY THE CLIMB?

MOST EXHILARATING, THANK YOU. I SAY—YOU HAVE BEEN BUSY. YOUR SHOOTING MUST BE IMPROVING. NOW, WHERE'S THAT WIRELESS SET? I HAVE A LITTLE MESSAGE TO BROADCAST TO THE GERMANS!

ATTENTION ALL ARTILLERY UNITS! THIS IS URGENT. DURING THE NIGHT, ENEMY COMMANDO UNITS HAVE INFILTRATED THE CLEFT IN THE HILLS. REQUEST IMMEDIATE SATURATION BOMBARDMENT ON THAT AREA.

LOOK AT 'IM, COOL AS A CUCUMBER. AIN'T 'E GOT NO NERVES?

BLIMEY—IT'S WORKING! THE JERRIES AIN'T 'ALF GIVING THEIR OWN MATES A PASTING. WHAT 'APPENS NEXT, GUV?

REALLY, BONES—YOU ARE AN IMPATIENT FELLOW. WAIT AND SEE!

TRANSPORTS! WE'RE SENDING IN THE PARATROOPS WHILE THE JERRY GUNS ARE FIRING ON THEIR OWN MEN. THEY SHOULD CAPTURE THEM GUNS IN NO TIME.

EXACTLY! AND THEN WE WILL LAUNCH AN ALL-OUT TANK ATTACK THROUGH THE CLEFT. SIMPLE, BUT EFFECTIVE.

THE RACE THAT LASTED A YEAR

THIRTEEN-year-old Chris Stafford knew how hard it was to keep a secret, but not even Mister Petrie, his P.E. master at Harcrosse School, was going to make him reveal his plan before time!

"Look, Stafford," Mister Petrie was saying, "when are you going to stop fooling around and try harder on these runs? I could use you in the school team."

"But, sir," Chris rather half-heartedly replied, "I'm not interested in running. I'm no good anyway. I'd rather play football."

Mister Petrie was angry as well as being in a hurry to get away and dismissed Chris, saying, "You never want to do anything for the school! That's where your loyalty should lie. Don't expect me to do anything for you."

"Ah, nuts!" Chris said to himself as Petrie walked off. "Why can't he leave me alone? I don't want to run in his lousy cross-country team anyway. I'm better than all of them!"

* * * * *

Six months before, during the summer term, Chris had been persuaded to run the half-mile in the school sports. Although Chris was just over thirteen years old, his small size and thin body made him appear to be much weaker and more frail than he actually was. Philip Rayner, a bigger and older boy in another form in the same year at school, never missed an opportunity to tease him about it. Unhappily for Chris, Rayner had also entered for the same race and took great delight in making fun of Chris's chances.

"You'll never manage to crawl round two laps, let alone run!" he would jeer, or else he would mockingly call after him, "Come and see the midget half-miler!"

Of course, remarks like these made Chris very angry, but he knew there was no way he could get

his own back in the race for Rayner was far too big and strong to be beaten. He dreaded the approach of the sports and his likely humiliation in front of the entire school as well as the prospect of even more of the same bullying treatment afterwards.

So, on the day of the sports, Chris, unable to avoid taking part, joined battle with Rayner and six other boys. Whilst Chris and the others waited nervously near the start, Rayner was striding about doing limbering-up exercises.

As they lined up to start, Rayner, elbowing his way into the inside lane, looked across at Chris and muttered, "Don't take too long or we'll have to send out a search party!"

Before Chris could make any kind of reply, the gun went off and Rayner dashed into the lead, leaving the rest to settle into a more steady pace.

Chris, however, stung by

Rayner's remark, tore after him, determined to stay with him and get even. But Chris, running as hard as he could, was soon overtaken by tiredness and began to hang on desperately to Rayner's easier stride. As they entered the second lap, Chris could keep going no longer and collapsed, exhausted, on to the centre of the track and lay there on his back panting heavily, feeling very angry, hating Rayner and fighting back the tears.

As he struggled to get on to his feet and disappear before Rayner had a chance to come across and boast about his win, Chris saw Petrie bearing down on him.

"What do you think you're doing, Stafford?" he almost shouted. "Don't you realise that you've cost your house points? You shouldn't take part if you're not going to finish."

Chris was far too fed-up and out of breath to say anything in reply. In any case, Petrie rushed off, so Chris was able to slip away before anyone else had a chance to tell him off or make fun of him.

Good Advice!

LATER, when Chris returned home for tea, his mother, who had been in the crowd watching the sports, asked him, "Why did you drop out, love? You were going so well. I'm sure that you could have won if you'd kept running."

"It's no good, Mum," moaned Chris. "He's too big, and he annoyed me. I shouldn't have chased after him like that."

Over tea Chris told his mother about Rayner's bullying and why he was angry with him during the race. Later that evening as he lay in bed reliving the misery of his defeat, his dad came in to say goodnight.

"Look, son, I know you're upset," he sympathised, "but don't let it get you down. You can't bear a grudge all your life, you know. Have you ever thought how nice it would be if you could run like Rayner and win?"

"Oh, come off it, Dad! I haven't got a chance against a great brute like that."

"No, of course not, if you believe you haven't; but you've never done much running, so you just don't know how good you could be with a bit of practice. Your mum says that you were running really well until you gave up.

"Why don't you try some running between now and the next sports? Then go out and show him who's best? That's better than being angry with yourself and doing nothing about it or calling him names in return. Isn't it?"

"Yes, I know, Dad," Chris wearily replied, "but I'm just not good enough."

"Look, I'll tell you what I'll do," said his father. "There's a chap at work called Dave Aubrey who knows quite a lot about running. He coaches some lads down at the sports arena. I'll ask him if he can help. What do you say?"

"Okay, Dad," said Chris, drifting off to sleep, hoping that this would end the matter.

However, Chris's dad had been serious and when Chris met Dave Aubrey and realised how nice and friendly he was, the idea of actually running in order to get fit did not seem so silly after all. Dave, who had been an athlete himself and still took part in the odd club run, had a jolly, easy-going way with boys. He kept the interest and enjoyment in their running by varying the training and by not expecting too much of them.

Chris soon became a regular visitor to the Sunday morning training sessions at the arena, and sometimes he could even be seen there on Saturdays or during the holidays. Nor was it unusual to see him slipping out for an evening run, or climbing over the fence into the local sports ground for some fast striding on the grass.

Dave explained to Chris that, often, boys like Rayner never bothered to train because success came easily to them, but that they could soon be overtaken by someone who was prepared to work in order to improve.

As Chris got fitter, Dave asked him to run in some of the boys' races with the club, but Chris said "No," and clung to his plan to train secretly then spring a great surprise on both Rayner and Petrie. He didn't want to spoil this by letting them know how good he really was.

One day during the Easter holiday, Chris's father took a walk down to the arena to see how training was progressing. Chris was sitting on the grass together with the only boy who shared his secret, his closest friend, Pete Graves.

"How's it going then?" his father called across.

"Dave says I'm coming along all right," replied Chris. "He thinks I should run for the club."

"Will you?" asked his father.

"No, I'm not going to bother," Chris said, lying back on the grass.

Chris soon became a regular at the training sessions held at the local sports ground.

Last minute nerves took hold of Chris as he lined up for the big race!

"How about you, Pete," enquired Mister Stafford. "Are you going to do any running this year?"

"Oh, no!" exclaimed Pete. "That's too much like hard work."

"Well, Chris doesn't seem to think so," Mister Stafford replied with a smile and then turned away to continue on his walk.

Sports Day!

AS the day of the sports approached Chris's secret seemed to be safe, for Rayner gave no sign that he might know and continued to make sneering remarks like, "Are you going to make a fool of yourself again this year, Stafford?"

"Wait and see," was Chris's sharp reply.

However, Chris still had to make sure that he would be picked for the house team, so, plucking up courage, he asked Mister Haslam, the head of Newton House, "Sir, I was wondering if I could run the eight-eighty again in the sports this year."

"Well, after last year, I'm not so sure," Mister Haslam hesitated. "How do I know you won't let us down again?"

"I won't let you down, sir," pleaded Chris, "just give me a chance."

"All right, Stafford," nodded Mister Haslam, "I'm sure you want an opportunity to redeem yourself; but just you remember that everybody will be expecting you to fail. Don't give in this time, right?"

"I won't fail, sir, I promise I'll do my best," said Chris, feeling greatly relieved.

* * * * *

"For goodness sake pay attention, Stafford!" bellowed Mister Snaith, the maths master. "Now what have I been saying?"

It was the morning of the sports and Chris was lost in his dream race striding majestically down the finishing straight leaving Rayner and all the others far behind. Pete prodded him urgently, whispering, "Chris! Sniffy's talking to you."

"I'm sorry, sir," stammered out Chris. "What were you saying?"

"Have you heard anything I've been saying?" demanded Mister Snaith.

"No, sir." Chris apologised.

"Well, see me afterwards and, for once, listen to what I'm saying."

After the lesson, Pete waited for Chris and asked, "What did he say?"

"Oh, nothing," said Chris. "I've got to do some work for him by tomorrow."

Then, rapidly changing the subject, he asked, "Have you seen Rayner today? He wasn't in assembly. You don't think he's got wind of it, do you?"

"No, of course not," said Pete.

"He's probably helping old Petrie get things ready for this afternoon."

Chris sat alone during lunch, nervously prodding his food, unable to eat anything, gloomily thinking about his chances in the coming race and, for the first time, beginning to think that he might lose. Secretly he hoped that his parents would not be there to see this.

Although Chris's race was one of the earliest of the afternoon, the waiting seemed like hours, and he sat in the changing-room alone rather than wait outside with his class-mates. His peace was soon disturbed, however, by Pete, who burst in excitedly shouting, "He's not running, he's not in school."

"Who, Rayner?" Chris demanded, glaring at Pete.

"Yes! Perkins, in his form, says that his mother phoned in to say he's off sick."

"Rubbish!" growled Chris. "He's chickened out! He must have known. What a rotten trick!"

"He could be ill," Pete said rather weakly. "Perkins says he went home early yesterday because he felt sick."

"He's just a coward!" Chris angrily retorted, and got up from the bench he was sitting on and walked away, calling back, "What's the point of running now?"

As he walked, dejectedly, out to the track, Chris heard his name being called and looked across to see his parents coming towards him.

"We thought we'd surprise you," his mother said cheerfully and then, seeing his face, enquired, "What's the matter? You look really miserable."

"Oh, it's Rayner," Chris said, looking even more unhappy. "He's not running. He's supposed to be sick."

"It doesn't matter, Chris," his father said, trying to cheer things up. "It's the race that's important. Go out and show them who's really the best. You don't want to waste all that training, do you?"

"Go on, Chris," his mother urged. "Go out and win for us. Go out and run faster than Rayner ever did, then you'll know you're better."

"You know we're behind you; don't let us down," his father added.

"Yes, you're probably right,"

Chris said, brightening up. "I can still show old Petrie that he was wrong about me."

"Good luck, Chris," they called after him.

The Race!

WITHOUT Rayner in the race the only threat to Chris's chances of winning was likely to come from Tony Rodgers, a tall, long-striding runner who was a regular member of the school team.

At the command, "On your marks!" the runners shuffled forward to the line. Chris could see, out of the corner of his eye, Rodgers leaning forward, ready for a fast start. But his own eagerness was almost his undoing as, on the word "Set!" he nearly toppled over the line and was regaining his balance when the gun went off. Chris soon recovered, but found himself at the back of a slow-moving bunch of runners as no one seemed to want to lead.

Down at the arena Dave had advised him to run his own race and not to pay too much attention to what the other runners were doing. But now he was confused and unsure whether to follow the rest or to run the way he felt and to take the lead.

This doubt only lasted for a few seconds, for Rodgers, unhappy with the slow pace, accelerated into a lead and, by the time Chris had responded and moved to the head of the chasing group, Rodgers was almost ten yards clear.

As they rounded the top bend with a quarter of the race over, Chris was feeling good, but Rodgers was moving well and maintaining his lead. Beginning slowly to eat up the lead, Chris passed the bell only five yards down; but, encouraged by the shouts of the crowd, Rodgers was holding his form and looked set to win.

Along the back straight, Chris, chasing hard, closed the gap and tucked himself in behind Rodgers, resisting the temptation to overtake. As they entered the final bend at the farthest point from the crowd, a lone staff voice called out, "Good running, Stafford! Go hard all the way."

As if encouraged by this support, Chris moved up to Rodgers' shoulder and then, within a few strides, found himself in front.

Off the bend and into the finishing straight Chris sprinted hard, punching his arms back and forth, running for all he was worth towards the cluster of officials grouped around the tape. The sound of the crowd was almost completely shut out from his hearing by the noise of his own heavy breathing and by his concentration on holding his sprint to the line.

As he breasted the tape, he threw his arms jubilantly into the air and coasted down to a walk, feeling almost overcome by the sense of sheer elation from running hard and winning. Ignoring everything else but the rapid thump thump of his pummelling heart, he walked off the track into the centre of the arena, not even bothering to look back to see a weary Rodgers finishing nearly thirty yards behind, and lay on his back breathing in great gulps of air, feeling happier than he had been in a long time.

He looked up, a broad smile on his face, to see Mister Petrie standing over him and heard the wonderful words of congratulation, "Well done, Stafford, that was a splendid piece of running, and a real surprise. Have you been saving this up for us?"

"I've been training, sir," puffed out Chris.

"I'll say you have," Mister Petrie beamed back at him, "that run was good enough to win the district sports. Do you want me to enter you now?"

"If you like, sir," Chris replied, too excited by his win to care, but glad to have shown old Petrie what he was really capable of.

"You were terrific," said Pete, who had dashed across the track from where he had been throwing the javelin in order to share in his friend's success, "you left them standing. I'd like to see Rayner's face when he hears about this."

As Chris began to walk back towards the changing-rooms, he could hear over the tannoy system the announcement, "The winner of the boys' under-fifteen eight-eighty yards — Stafford, of Newton House, in a new school record of . . ." but the rest was lost amid the applause.

On the way home after the end of the sports, as Chris sat back in his father's car still feeling on top of the world, his father asked him, "Well, how do you feel now — tired?"

"Just great, Dad," replied Chris, as if this wasn't obvious.

"Yes, but I'll bet that you'll be stiff in the morning," his mother said good-humouredly.

"And what about big bully Rayner now?" asked his father as they pulled into the driveway of their home.

"I don't really care," said Chris, "it doesn't matter any more."

The END

IT'S A FUNNY OLD

Without the aid of D.D.T. or any other chemicals, a Japanese man swatted 180,003 flies in one day— a record likely to stand for some time.

JAPAN.

To toughen up his men, an American football coach gave them a real live elephant to push around. He also thought up a way to teach them the art of swerving on the run— he got them to chase live chickens.

U.S.A.

If any prisoners escape from the jail in Alamos, the guards who are on duty during the escape have to serve the remaining terms of the jail-breakers.

MEXICO.

GUARD

ECUADOR.

Police in Quito, hunting for a thief who stole nothing but pairs of shoes, found the missing articles in the kennel of a dog owned by one of their own officers. The dog is to receive corrective training.

EL POLIZIA CHIEFIES DOGENZA

NEW ZEALAND.

Bennie Jarvis spent three weeks on crutches after taking a mighty swipe at a golf ball—he missed and crushed his toe instead. Back in action on a course near Auckland, he again tried a mighty drive and lost hold of his club which flew into the branches of a tree. He climbed the tree to get it, but poor Bennie fell and broke his leg.

BRAZIL.

Manuel Sanos, a Brazilian weight-lifter, has lost his job as the village bellringer. Twice in three months, his extra strong tugs pulled down the bells, despite warnings to take it easy.

62

WORLD WE LIVE IN !

An eager young newspaper reporter on his first assignment drove the firm's car to a car-crushing plant, parked in the wrong place and went to interview the manager. He returned in time to see the vehicle being squashed for scrap. It was his last assignment!

BRITAIN.

After clearing 6 ft. 8 ins., his personal best, high-jumper Wolfgang Schwalbe hurried home to tell his wife. While hurdling his 2 ft. 6 ins. gate, he tripped and broke his ankle.

W. GERMANY.

A concert rehearsal in Warsaw was postponed when Sergei Rakalowski accidently "sandwiched" the head of the French horn player in front of him with his cymbals. At the time, the orchestra was rehearsing Tchaikovsky's "Nutcracker Suite"!

POLAND

Spanish dancer Juan Arave tried to establish a new marathon record of tapping his heels—but angry neighbours brought his attempt to a halt. After Juan had been heel-tapping for 27 hours, the noise on their ceiling finally drove them mad, so they rushed upstairs to Juan's flat and tied him to his bed to keep him quiet.

SPAIN.

Cleto Mancelli was ordered by wrestling officials to keep his teenage daughters, Anna and Carlotta, away from an Italian wrestling arena because they kept climbing into the ring and sticking brooch-pins into the rumps of wrestlers whom they disliked.

ITALY.

ROUND THE WORLD OR BUST

INDIA.

An Indian, Hari Rahman, planned to cycle round the world. Twelve seconds after a tumultuous send-off, he had to give up because he buckled both wheels of his bike when he collided with a photographer's car.

KILLER KENNEDY R.N.

TWO GERMAN R-BOATS AHEAD, SIR! LAYING MINES!

WE'VE FOUND OUR TARGET! ACTION STATIONS! FULL AHEAD!

During the Second World War, Lieutenant-Commander "Killer" Kennedy commanded a motor torpedo boat, with Sub-Lieutenant Bill Doyle as his junior officer. One night they were patrolling off the east coast of England.

OPEN FIRE AS YOUR GUNS BEAR!

THAT'S ONE KNOCKED OUT BUT THE OTHER ONE'S MAKING A RUN FOR IT!

THEY'RE HOPING WE'LL RUN ON TO THE MINES THEY'VE LAID ASTERN! HARD OVER, COX'N! WE'LL CIRCLE CLEAR BEFORE WE FOLLOW.

THEY'RE OPENING FIRE, AND THEY'VE GOT HEAVIER STUFF THAN WE CARRY!

THEY CAN'T OUT-RUN US. WE WON'T WASTE A TORPEDO. AIM AT HER STERN.

HER REMAINING MINES HAVE BLOWN UP!

GOOD SHOOTING, LADS! DOYLE, GET OFF A SIGNAL GIVING OUR POSITION. THE MINESWEEPERS CAN COME AND COLLECT THE LAID MINES.

E

Kennedy waited until the minesweepers arrived at dawn.

THE MINESWEEPERS' PARAVANES ARE BRINGING THE MINES TO THE SURFACE.

WE'LL GIVE OUR LADS SOME MORE SHOOTING PRACTICE.

GOT IT! THAT'S THE LAST MINE, SIR.

THE CONVOY LANES ARE CLEAR AGAIN. WE CAN GO HOME.

The M.T.B. returned to its east coast base.

HARBOUR WATCH ONLY, DOYLE. THE REST OF THE LADS CAN GET A MEAL AND A SLEEP AFTER WE CHECK GUNS AND ENGINES.

AYE, AYE, SIR. HULLO, HERE COMES COMMANDER BUDD.

Commander Budd had a desk job in the Port Admiral's office.

WE'RE PUTTING ON A SHOW FOR A SENIOR OFFICIAL OF THE ADMIRALTY WHO'S ARRIVING TODAY, KENNEDY. YOU'LL SEND A DETACHMENT OF YOUR MEN TO JOIN THE PARADE.

WE'VE BEEN AT SEA ALL NIGHT—IN ACTION, TOO, IF YOU'RE INTERESTED! AND WE'RE ON PATROL AGAIN TONIGHT. I CAN'T SPARE ANYBODY.

YOUR MEN WILL BE ON PARADE, KENNEDY! THAT'S AN ORDER!

CRIKEY, THE SKIPPER'S TAKING IT WITHOUT A MURMUR! THAT'S NOT LIKE HIM!

The parade assembled.

OUR VISITOR IS DUE. IS THE PARADE READY?

ALL EXCEPT KENNEDY'S DETACHMENT, SIR. ER—HERE THEY COME NOW!

WHAT DO YOU MEAN BY TURNING UP LIKE A SET OF SCARECROWS, KENNEDY?

HAD TO BREAK OFF OUR MAINTENANCE WORK TO BE HERE. WE HAD NO TIME TO TIDDLEY UP, BUT REPORTING AS ORDERED, COMMANDER!

HERE COMES OUR VISITOR. GET YOUR SCRUFFS OUT OF SIGHT, KENNEDY! YOU'LL HEAR MORE OF THIS.

AYE, AYE! BACK TO WORK, LADS—AT THE DOUBLE!

Later.

BUDD COMPLAINS YOU TRIED TO MAKE A FOOL OF HIM AT THE PARADE, KENNEDY.

TIME ENOUGH FOR PARADES WHEN WE'VE WON THE WAR, SIR. MY MEN HAVE GOT MORE IMPORTANT THINGS TO DO.

ALL CLOSED UP AND READY FOR SEA, SIR!

I HAVEN'T BEEN RELIEVED OF MY COMMAND, IF THAT'S WHAT YOU'RE THINKING, DOYLE. THE FLOTILLA CAPTAIN'S GOT MORE SENSE THAN BUDD. RIGHT, HANDS TO STATIONS FOR LEAVING HARBOUR!

That night.

A QUIET NIGHT, SIR. DAWN'S COMING UP, AND WE HAVEN'T SEEN A THING.

LOOKS AS IF THE MINELAYERS HAVE BEEN FRIGHTENED OFF. SET COURSE FOR HOME.

YOUR GUNS HAVEN'T BEEN FIRED, KENNEDY. SO MUCH FOR YOUR FIGHTING TALK!

HAVEN'T SEEN THE ENEMY ALL NIGHT, BUDD— UNTIL NOW!

The M.T.B. was on patrol again the next night.

ANOTHER QUIET NIGHT, SIR. HERE'S ONE OF OUR COASTAL CONVOYS COMING OVER THE HORIZON.

THEY'LL HAVE A CLEAR PASSAGE.

But—

ONE OF THE SHIPS HAS BEEN HIT!

A MINE!

ANOTHER MINE! ONE OF THE DESTROYER ESCORT THIS TIME!

SIGNAL THE CONVOY TO HEAVE TO! THEY CAN'T PROCEED UNTIL THE MINES HAVE BEEN SWEPT. WE'LL GO IN AND PICK UP SURVIVORS BUT SLOWLY—WE DON'T WANT TO BE NUMBER THREE!

The M.T.B. returned to port with the survivors they had picked up.

YOU'RE RESPONSIBLE FOR THE MINELAYERS GETTING THROUGH, KENNEDY.

I KNOW IT. AND I'M NOT AS PLEASED ABOUT IT AS YOU SEEM TO BE, BUDD!

The M.T.B. patrolled for two more nights without incident then—

AN EXPLOSION, SIR! MINES AGAIN!

BY THUNDER! AND WE DIDN'T SEE A THING!

THE CAPTAIN WANTS TO SEE YOU, KENNEDY!

BUDD IS REALLY GLOATING NOW!

I'VE MADE A REPORT ON ALL THE SINKINGS BY MINES WHILE KENNEDY HAS BEEN ON PATROL, SIR.

I SHAN'T NEED THAT, BUDD, BUT SOMETHING'S GOING WRONG, KENNEDY. THE SEA'S A BIG PLACE, I KNOW, BUT IT'S YOUR JOB TO STOP THOSE MINELAYERS GETTING THROUGH.

I'M MAKING NO EXCUSES, SIR. I'VE BEEN OUTSMARTED SO FAR BUT I MEAN TO FIND THE MINELAYERS.

SEE THAT YOU DO. IF YOU CAN'T COPE, I'M SENDING OUT ANOTHER BOAT IN YOUR PLACE.

68

YOU WON'T GET ANOTHER SEA-GOING COMMAND, KENNEDY. BUT THERE'S A VACANCY IN MY OFFICE—MAKING THE TEA!

The M.T.B. sailed again.

OUR RADAR HASN'T PICKED UP ANY MINELAYING AIRCRAFT, SO IT MUST BE A SHIP. COULD BE A SUBMARINE SNEAKING IN, SIR. CONDITIONS ARE SUITABLE, SAME AS LAST NIGHT. LESS CLOUD, BUT NO SEA RUNNING, WIND LIGHT FROM THE EAST.

WIND FROM THE EAST! THE SAME AS ON THE OTHER NIGHTS WHEN MINES WERE LAID! STOP ENGINES!

YOU THINK THE GERMANS ARE USING THE WEATHER CONDITIONS IN SOME WAY, SIR? CRIKEY, NOT A SAILING SHIP! THAT WOULD BE SILENT ENOUGH.

SOUNDS UNLIKELY. BUT THEY'VE GOT SOME TRICK UP THEIR SLEEVE. WE'LL LIE DOGGO, AND KEEP EYES AND EARS OPEN. HERE COMES THE MOON.

The M.T.B. lay motionless, silent and watchful.

LOOK, SIR! AN AIRSHIP!

A GERMAN ZEPPELIN! DRIFTING IN ON THE WIND WITH ENGINES STOPPED.

SHE'S COMING DOWN.

PREPARING TO LAY MINES. START ENGINES. FULL AHEAD!

SHE'S RISING AGAIN. HER ENGINES HAVE STARTED. WE'VE BEEN SPOTTED.

THEY WON'T MINE OUR SEA LANES THIS TIME, ANYWAY! OPEN FIRE!

69

ACCORDING TO THE MAPS, THE 1918 AIRSHIP BASE WAS JUST INLAND FROM HERE. COME ON, LADS.

THIS IS IT. THE OLD SHEDS ARE STILL IN USE. LOOK, THEY'RE HOUSING THE ZEPP.

NOT MUCH CHANCE OF GETTING AT IT, SIR. LIGHTS AND SENTRIES EVERYWHERE.

THERE'S A CAR LEAVING. SOME OF THE AIRSHIP CREW, PROBABLY. QUICK, BACK ALONG THE ROAD, AWAY FROM THE LIGHTS!

HIMMEL! A BODY IN THE ROAD! STOP!

SIT STILL, FRITZ!

WHAT?

MOVE A MUSCLE AND WE'LL OPEN FIRE!

RIGHT. THAT'S US IN THEIR UNIFORMS, NOW INTO THE CAR!

CHANGED YOUR MIND ABOUT BREAKFAST IN TOWN, KAPITAN? ACH, BUT WHO ARE YOU?

PUT YOUR FOOT DOWN, ROGERS!

The M.T.B. returned safely to base

A SHOT IN A MILLION!

I'VE DONE IT!

In 1839, Private Ben Ferris was serving with the British Army in Afghanistan. Ben, an ace marksman, was now demonstrating his skill to three tribesmen allies of the British . . .

THE FERRINGHEE HAS A SURE EYE AND A STEADY HAND.

AND YOU, MY FRIEND, HAVE A STEADY NERVE.

Lieutenant Claude Pomeroy, a cowardly and brutal officer, suddenly appeared.

WHAT DO YOU MEAN, FERRIS, BY SHOOTING OUT HERE WHERE THE ENEMY CAN SEE YOU? AND YOU DOGS, BACK TO YOUR QUARTERS AT ONCE. YOU AND YOUR BROTHER, FERRIS, ARE A DISGRACE TO THE ARMY. ANY MORE TROUBLE AND I'LL HAVE YOU FLOGGED!

POMEROY'S HAD IT IN FOR ME ALL ALONG. I WAS DOING NO HARM, BUT I'D BETTER GET AWAY QUICKLY.

An hour later, Ben's young brother, Johnny, bumped into Lieutenant Pomeroy.

YOUR PARDON, SIR, BUT I AM SEEKING MY BROTHER, BEN. DO YOU KNOW IF HE IS ON DUTY?

ON DUTY? I'LL GIVE HIM DUTY WHEN I GET MY HANDS ON HIM! HE WAS INSOLENT ENOUGH TO MARCH OFF WITHOUT ORDERS UP THE PASS. LOOKS TO ME LIKE THE DOG'S DESERTED!

DESERTION! IT CAN'T BE TRUE! BEN'S THE BEST SHOT IN THE ARMY. THE ARMY IS HIS LIFE. I MUST FIND HIM AND BRING HIM BACK TO CAMP BEFORE IT'S TOO LATE!

BEN! BEN, IT'S YOUR BROTHER. COME BACK TO THE CAMP.

73

WHAT WAS THAT? I HEARD SOMETHING! SOUNDS LIKE SOMEBODY MOVING UP THERE.

Suddenly . . .

NOT ANOTHER STEP, FERRINGHEE, OR YOU DIE!

IT WAS A TRICK! WHAT A FOOL I'VE BEEN!

I HAVE NOT FOUND MY BROTHER, BUT I HAVE SEALED MY OWN DEATH WARRANT! I'LL NEVER SEE THE CAMP AGAIN!

In 1838, the British Army had marched into Afghanistan to oust Dost Mohammed from the throne at Kabul and instal their own puppet ruler, Sujah ul Mulk. Now they were close to the fortress of Ghazni, astride the road to Kabul. It had to be taken quickly because the British column was almost out of food. Now, the British and Sujah ul Mulk's men prepared to break camp.

As they did so, Ben Ferris, unaware of his brother's fate, was searching for him.

BLIMEY! THEY SAID YOU'D DESERTED, BEN! POMEROY'S GOT A THOUSAND LASHES IN STORE FOR YOU!

I DIDN'T DESERT. I JUST WENT TO COOL OFF. HAVE YOU SEEN JOHNNY? THERE'S NO SIGN OF THE YOUNG RIP!

HALT WHERE YOU ARE, FERRIS! SO YOU CAME BACK! WELL, THAT WON'T DO YOU ANY GOOD—

A SHOT!

Before the Afghans could recover their wits . . .

QUICK, JOHNNY. FOLLOW ME! WE MUST GET OUT OF HERE AND UP TO THE WALL OF THE FORTRESS. THE ARMY'S OUTSIDE! THOSE DOGS'LL HAVE NO TIME TO HUNT FOR US DURING THE BATTLE!

Outside, Captain Donnelly of Ben's regiment was giving instructions to some volunteers.

THE FORTRESS IS IMPREGNABLE— WHILE THE KANDAHAR GATE STANDS. WE ARE GOING TO BLOW THAT GATE UP! THE OTHERS WILL GIVE US COVERING FIRE!

WHEN WE REACH THE SHELTER OF THE GATE DROP YOUR SACKS IN POSITION. THEN MAKE A RUN FOR IT!

THERE GO MY AFGHAN FRIENDS. NOW IT ONLY REMAINS FOR CAPTAIN DONNELLY TO FIRE THE GUNPOWDER. LUCKILY THIS POSITION WE HOLD IS THE ONLY ONE WHICH OVERLOOKS HIM.

NOW TO LAY A TRAIL OF GUNPOWDER—THEN TO BLOW UP THE GATE!

But . . .

OH, NO! THE CAPTAIN'S BEEN HIT BY A STRAY BULLET FROM THE BRITISH COVERING FIRE. IT'S ALL BEEN FOR NOTHING!

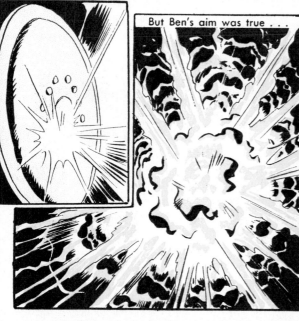

THE END

QUICK QUIZ

ANSWERS ON PAGE 48

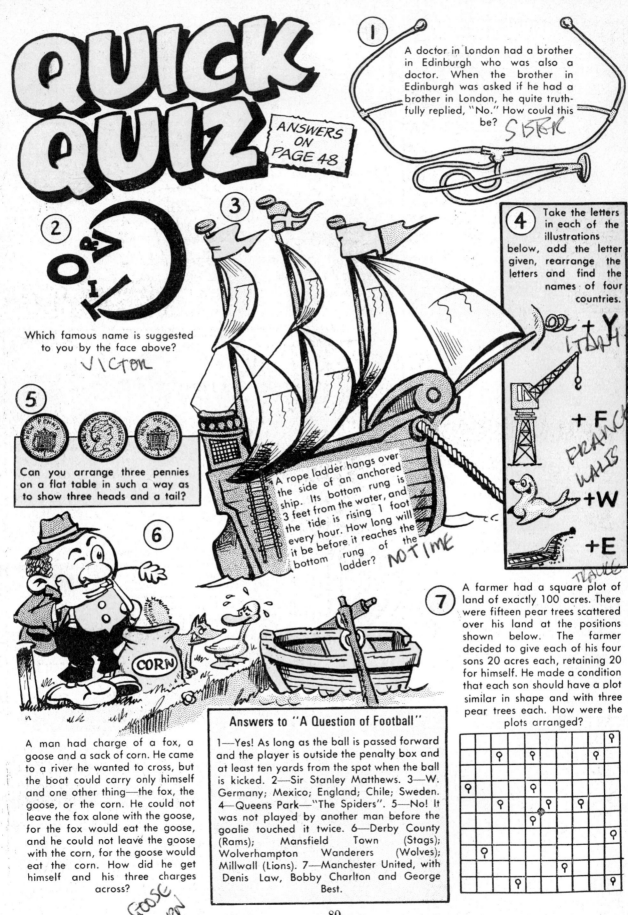

1 A doctor in London had a brother in Edinburgh who was also a doctor. When the brother in Edinburgh was asked if he had a brother in London, he quite truthfully replied, "No." How could this be?

2 Which famous name is suggested to you by the face above?

4 Take the letters in each of the illustrations below, add the letter given, rearrange the letters and find the names of four countries.

+Y

+F

+W

+E

5 Can you arrange three pennies on a flat table in such a way as to show three heads and a tail?

A rope ladder hangs over the side of an anchored ship. Its bottom rung is 3 feet from the water, and the tide is rising 1 foot every hour. How long will it be before it reaches the bottom rung of the ladder?

6 A man had charge of a fox, a goose and a sack of corn. He came to a river he wanted to cross, but the boat could carry only himself and one other thing—the fox, the goose, or the corn. He could not leave the fox alone with the goose, for the fox would eat the goose, and he could not leave the goose with the corn, for the goose would eat the corn. How did he get himself and his three charges across?

CORN

7 A farmer had a square plot of land of exactly 100 acres. There were fifteen pear trees scattered over his land at the positions shown below. The farmer decided to give each of his four sons 20 acres each, retaining 20 for himself. He made a condition that each son should have a plot similar in shape and with three pear trees each. How were the plots arranged?

Answers to "A Question of Football"

1—Yes! As long as the ball is passed forward and the player is outside the penalty box and at least ten yards from the spot when the ball is kicked. 2—Sir Stanley Matthews. 3—W. Germany; Mexico; England; Chile; Sweden. 4—Queens Park—"The Spiders". 5—No! It was not played by another man before the goalie touched it twice. 6—Derby County (Rams); Mansfield Town (Stags); Wolverhampton Wanderers (Wolves); Millwall (Lions). 7—Manchester United, with Denis Law, Bobby Charlton and George Best.

THE PILOT FROM THE PAST

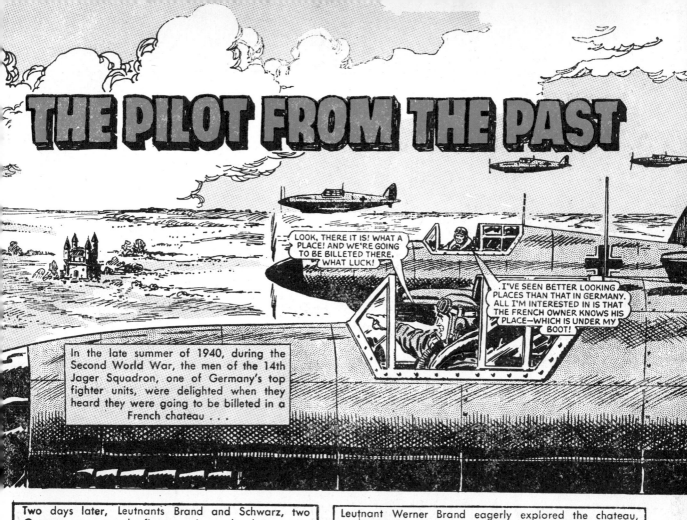

LOOK, THERE IT IS! WHAT A PLACE! AND WE'RE GOING TO BE BILLETED THERE. WHAT LUCK!

I'VE SEEN BETTER LOOKING PLACES THAN THAT IN GERMANY. ALL I'M INTERESTED IN IS THAT THE FRENCH OWNER KNOWS HIS PLACE—WHICH IS UNDER MY BOOT!

In the late summer of 1940, during the Second World War, the men of the 14th Jager Squadron, one of Germany's top fighter units, were delighted when they heard they were going to be billeted in a French chateau . . .

Two days later, Leutnants Brand and Schwarz, two German aces, were the first to arrive at the chateau . . .

PLEASE TREAT THE CHATEAU AS YOUR OWN, GENTLEMEN. YOU ARE HONOURED GUESTS HERE.

WE'LL HAVE NO TROUBLE WITH THIS ONE, WERNER. HE HASN'T THE GUTS OF A RABBIT!

SHUT UP, OTTO—HE'LL HEAR YOU.

Leutnant Werner Brand eagerly explored the chateau, moving rapidly from room to room, until...

HENRI D'ENGREMONT

IT'S LIKE A FIRST WORLD WAR MUSEUM OF FLYING! NOW WHY ON EARTH—OF COURSE! HENRI D'ENGREMONT! HE WAS THE FRENCH ACE OF ACES! NOW HOW MANY OF OUR PLANES DID HE SHOOT DOWN? 93–94?

...IT WAS 97, ACTUALLY. MY FATHER WAS A REMARKABLE FIGHTER PILOT. YOU ARE INTERESTED IN SUCH THINGS, MONSIEUR, EVEN IN THE EXPLOITS OF YOUR ENEMIES?

I AM INDEED AND I WOULD BE DELIGHTED IF YOU WOULD SHOW ME ROUND.

...AND THAT'S THE NIEUPORT BEBE THAT HE ALWAYS FLEW. IT ONLY HAD A LEWIS GUN WITH FORTY-SEVEN ROUNDS IN THE DRUM—BUT FATHER ALWAYS SAID A GOOD PILOT ONLY NEED USE SIX BULLETS TO GET A KILL. THE ACTUAL LEWIS GUN IS BENEATH THE PICTURE.

One day, as Werner was going to meet Raoul D'Engremont in the trophy room . . .

STOP IT, I SAY. YOU'VE NO RIGHT TO DO THAT!

BE QUIET, LITTLE FRENCH WORM! NOBODY TELLS ME WHAT I CAN OR CANNOT DO. THIS DART PRACTICE AMUSES ME.

SOMETIMES, OTTO, YOU MAKE ME VERY ASHAMED TO BE A GERMAN. RAOUL—ARE YOU ALL RIGHT?

I—I THINK SO. BUT LOOK WHAT HE'S DONE TO THE PICTURE. IT'S RUINED!

LISTEN TO ME, OTTO SCHWARZ. YOU HAVE INSULTED MY FATHER'S MEMORY. HE WILL NOT REST EASY IN HIS GRAVE TILL YOU ARE DEAD. YOUR DAYS, MY FRIEND, ARE NUMBERED!

Otto only laughed at this warning. That night . . .

WHO'S THERE? WHAT DO YOU MEAN BY BURSTING INTO MY ROOM IN THE MIDDLE OF THE NIGHT? STOP AND EXPLAIN YOURSELF!

HE'S VANISHED! AND THAT UNIFORM—IT WAS LIKE THE ONE IN THE PAINTING. WHAT'S HAPPENING TO ME?

Otto immediately woke up Werner to tell him what had happened . . .

BUT, WERNER—I SAW HIM! THE LITTLE FRENCHMAN'S FATHER! HE'S COMING TO GET ME, JUST AS RAOUL D'ENGREMONT PROMISED.

YOU HAVE SIMPLY HAD A BAD DREAM, OTTO. PERHAPS THIS WILL TEACH YOU NOT TO BE SUCH A BULLY. NOW, GO AND GET SOME SLEEP.

But at dusk next evening, returning from a mission over England . . .

WERNER—LOOK! IT'S A FIRST WORLD WAR NIEUPORT—JUST LIKE HENRI D'ENGREMONT FLEW. I'M BEING HAUNTED!

THEN I'M BEING HAUNTED AS WELL, BECAUSE I CAN SEE IT TOO. THERE'S SOMETHING FUNNY GOING ON HERE! LET'S TRY AND FOLLOW IT.

82

LOST IT! IT MUST HAVE GONE INTO THAT CLOUD. COME ON, OTTO—LET'S GET BACK TO THE AIRFIELD. THIS MUST BE REPORTED TO THE STATION COMMANDER.

...AND THEN THE BI-PLANE DISAPPEARED INTO THE CLOUD. SIR—I THINK I AM BEING HAUNTED.

GENTLEMEN, YOU HAVE BOTH FLOWN TOO MANY MISSIONS AND YOUR NERVES ARE AT BREAKING POINT. YOU ARE IMAGINING THINGS. SHORTLY, I WILL BE SENDING YOU BOTH ON TWO WEEKS LEAVE. THAT WILL CURE YOU. DISMISS!

I'VE GOT TO SEE YOU BOTH. PLEASE COME TO THE TROPHY ROOM AT ONCE.

ALL RIGHT, RAOUL, BUT MAKE IT SHORT. WE'RE BOTH STILL TIRED AFTER THE MISSION.

I SPOKE HASTILY THE OTHER DAY. I DIDN'T MEAN WHAT I WAS SAYING ABOUT FATHER COMING BACK. BUT THE LEWIS GUN—HIS LEWIS GUN—IT'S GONE! AS IF HE INTENDED TO USE IT!

HE IS COMING TO GET ME! I AM A DEAD MAN!

The next day, Werner and Otto were again scheduled for a mission over England. The mission was uneventful, but on returning at dusk . . .

WERNER! HE'S ON MY TAIL! GET HIM OFF! GET HIM OFF!

I'M COMING, OTTO. TOO LATE—HE'S GOT HIM!

83

SHOT DOWN—AND BY A PILOT FROM THE PAST! NO, I DON'T BELIEVE IT. THERE'S FLESH AND BLOOD IN THAT OLD PLANE—AND I MEAN TO FIND OUT WHO!

I COULD OPEN FIRE NOW, BUT I WON'T. I WANT TO SEE WHO'S PILOTING IT!

TAXI-ING STRAIGHT INTO THE BARN, EH? FINE! ONCE I GET ON THE GROUND, I'LL HAVE YOU TRAPPED. THIS IS THE END OF YOU, MY PHANTOM FLYER!

I'M COMING IN TO GET YOU. BETTER PUT YOUR HANDS ABOVE YOUR HEAD, OTHERWISE YOU'RE A DEAD MAN!

IT'S NOT HERE! IT'S JUST VANISHED—AS IF IT HAD NEVER BEEN! DID I REALLY SEE IT—OR AM I IMAGINING THINGS, LIKE THE STATION COMMANDER SAYS?

The Station Commander had no doubts at all . . .

I BLAME MYSELF FOR OVER-WORKING YOU. TRY TO UNDER-STAND, LEUTNANT BRAND—THERE IS NO PHANTOM BI-PLANE. A SPITFIRE MUST HAVE GOT SCHWARZ, NOT THE OLD WRECK YOU IMAGINED. AT DUSK, THE LIGHT PLAYS SOME STRANGE TRICKS. YOU MUST RELAX—THE ORDERLY WILL GIVE YOU SOMETHING TO MAKE YOU SLEEP.

YOU THINK WHAT YOU WANT, SIR, BUT AS SOON AS I'VE RESTED I'M GOING BACK TO THE BARN!

Next evening . . .

NOTHING—JUST LIKE IT WAS BEFORE. AM I GOING MAD? NO! IT WASN'T A GHOST THAT KILLED OTTO. I THINK I'LL HAVE A LOOK AT THAT END WALL...

RAISE YOUR HANDS AND TURN ROUND—SLOWLY!

HENRI D'ENGREMONT— BUT YOU'RE DEAD!

NO, WERNER, IT IS RAOUL D'ENGREMONT, AND VERY MUCH ALIVE. COME, I HAVE SOMETHING TO SHOW YOU.

FATHER'S OLD PLANE—A BEAUTY, ISN'T SHE? SHE'LL FLY THE CHANNEL EASILY. SHE'S TAKEN ME MONTHS TO REPAIR—AND WEEKS TO LEARN HOW TO FLY. I HAD TO DO IT SECRETLY, OF COURSE—AND WHAT'S MORE SECRET THAN A GHOST?

FLY THE CHANNEL? BUT RAOUL, WHY?

SO THAT I CAN JOIN THE R.A.F. AND HELP TO FREE MY COUNTRY. OTTO SCHWARZ WAS ONLY MY FIRST KILL—THERE WILL BE MANY MORE. BUT I HOPE YOU WILL NEVER BE ONE OF THEM. LOOK AFTER YOURSELF, WERNER, AND NOW, OLD FELLOW, I'M AFRAID I MUST TIE YOU UP.

AND YOU TAKE CARE OF YOUR-SELF TOO, RAOUL. YOU'VE MADE FOOLS OF US ALL—BUT I CAN'T HELP ADMIRING YOU FOR IT.

THE END

AIR ACES
OF WORLD WAR ONE

WILLY COPPENS

The leading Belgian ace, Coppens' speciality was attacking barrage balloons. One day, on patrol, he spotted a German observation balloon and, ignoring heavy ground fire, approached to within 150 feet of his target and fired. The balloon erupted in flames!

ERNST UDET

Towards the end of the war, Udet, one of Germany's leading aces, destroyed a British tank at Villers-Cotterets. Six times he dived on the armoured giant before, out of control, it turned over.

R.A.J. WARNEFORD

The Russian Kazakov had the idea of bringing down enemy machines using a weighted anchor. Unfortunately, on its first operational flight in March, 1915, his device failed him when the anchor jammed. Undaunted, Kazakov rammed the opposing plane and destroyed it.

A.A. KAZAKOV

On June 7th, 1915, Warneford managed to get above a huge German Zeppelin and bomb it—despite its frantic efforts to escape. Warneford, the first airman in history to destroy a Zeppelin in flight, was later awarded the Victoria Cross.

MANFRED VON RICHTHOFEN

Manfred won Richthofen, the most famous German pilot, was known as the 'Red Baron'. His skill was matched on occasion by his luck. After his eighteenth victorious flight the wing of his Albatros D111 broke in the air, but he managed to descend safely.

CHARLES NUNGESSER

In May, 1917, Nungesser, a Frenchman, took up a challenge to single combat over Douai—only to find not one, but six German fighters awaiting him. Fighting for his life, Nungesser managed to shoot down two of his opponents and return safely to base.

RENÉ PAUL FONCK

René Paul Fonck, a Frenchman, was the highest scoring Allied pilot. Early in 1915, on reconnaissance, he met a German plane, but being unarmed, could do nothing. From then on he carried a rifle. Thus, on July 22nd, when he met a German two-seater, he was able to attack it using his rifle. His opponent fled.

WILLIAM AVERY BISHOP

On June 2nd, 1917, Bishop attacked a German aerodrome single-handed. After shooting up the planes on the ground, he shot down three others which attempted to intercept him. For this courageous action he was awarded the Victoria Cross.

THE HAMMER MAN

WHOA, GOLIATH! WHAT MEANS THIS OBSTRUCTION ON THE KING'S HIGHWAY, FRIEND?

Home from the wars in France in the time of King Henry the Fifth, master blacksmith Chell Puddock was riding through Chardwood Forest when . . .

IT MEANS 'TWILL COST YOU THIRTY PENCE IN TOLL MONEY TO HAVE THE ROCK REMOVED.

THIRTY PENNIES! 'TIS MORE THAN THE BRIDGE IS WORTH!

HO! HO! THE OAF THINKS TO REMOVE IT SINGLE-HANDED!

NOW YOU OWE ME THIRTY PENNIES FOR ITS REMOVAL!

ODDS TEETH! THAT ROCK WEIGHS TONS!

OUT OF THE WAY, MISCREANTS, OR OLD IRONHEAD HERE WILL TAP YOUR SCURVY SKULLS!

BARON BADDUN-VYLE SHALL HEAR OF THIS, YOU KNAVE!

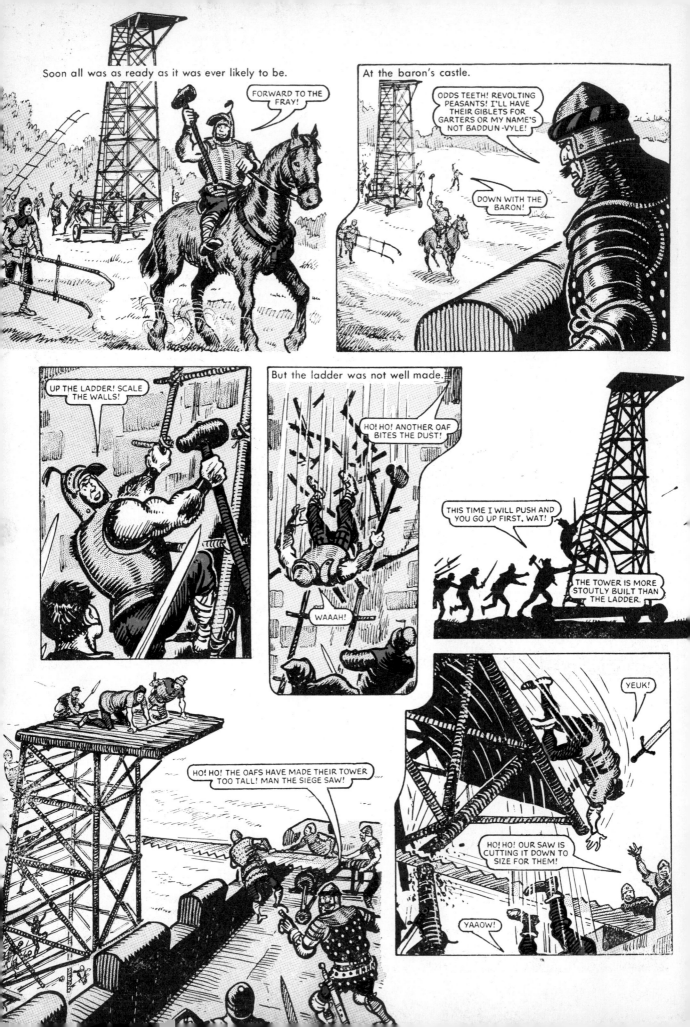

Boiling oil added to the attackers' discomfiture.

At the siege camp that night.

Later.

That gave Chell an idea.

Next day.

Chell found they had company in the dungeon.

Chell exerted all his mighty strength.

Up on the ramparts.

AAAH! THE KEEP QUAKES!

ODDS NOSE! WHAT HAPPENS?

WAAAGH!

GROOORGH!

CHARGE! THE KEEP IS BREACHED!

SO,'TWAS YOU WHO TOPPLED THE KEEP, CHELL!

AIDED BY THIS VENERABLE MASTER-BUILDER, HERE.

Soon, in the castle treasury—

HERE ARE THE MONIES STOLEN FROM MY FRIENDS AND ME.

WE SHALL MAKE GOODLY RECOMPENSE TO THEM—ALSO TO OUR MASTER-BUILDER HERE.

MY FEES AT LAST—AND WITH COMPOUND INTEREST!

So Sir Chell went his knightly way.

THERE GOES A TRUE AND GENTLE KNIGHT OFF TO MORE DEEDS OF DERRING-DO!

FAREWELL, FRIENDS! SEE TO IT THAT NOW YOU RETURN TO YOUR LAWFUL WAYS! GIDDUP, GOLIATH!

-THE END-

MIGHTY MUSCLES!

Alex Smith, of Perthshire, was a real "blowhard". He could blow up a rubber hot water bottle until it burst!

In August, 1971, Kenny Campbell, of Sutherland, carried a 200 lb. organ to the top of Ben Nevis. To celebrate his arrival at the summit he played "Scotland the Brave".

A real hard-headed fellow was the South African wrestler who used to amaze his friends by knocking in fence posts with his head!

A strongman act with real bite was performed by John Assis, of Belgium, in 1969. He pulled a 36-ton train along the track—with his teeth!

A building at Idle in Bradford was demolished recently by fifteen karate experts. It really got the chop!

Mrs Marie McArd, of Peterborough, was no seven and a half stone weakling. She could hold together two cars while the drivers tried to accelerate away!

Sergeant-Major Starkey, a highland games athlete in the 1920's, had an unusual visiting card. When he was asked for his card he would crumple up the tray he was meant to put it on.

SHOWDOWN AT SWEETWATER

ZEB TRAGG knew, deep down inside, that he was the fastest gunman around. He liked to show off to admiring loafers by shooting the spot from an ace, drilling a tossed coin neatly in the middle, or knocking the corks out of bottles without breaking the glass. But he had never shot a man!

Why waste his talents? There was no-one in any of the towns he'd passed through good enough to face him. Once they had seen him displaying his skills, few cared to try.

What he needed was to gun down a man with a reputation in a fair fight. Twice he'd come up against such a man, but a cold fear had gripped his innards each time and he had backed down and moved on in a hurry.

It had always been like that. Even as a kid he had had a mean, narrow-eyed expression which, coupled with his large, angular frame, made him appear a boy to be reckoned with. But he had backed out of fights with smaller, tougher kids even then.

He had taught himself to shoot, and had found that speed and accuracy came easily to him. It was just a question of mustering enough courage to face another man with a gun; to watch him draw with enough coldness in his heart to kill you without a care; to shoot him down first.

In spite of his failures, Tragg was still convinced he had it in him. As he idled on the sidewalk in Sweetwater watching an imposing-looking man ride slowly by, eyes darting everywhere as he passed, Tragg felt himself dismissed contemptuously by those eyes, and his anger mounted.

"Goodnight, Mister Kusselson," an old-timer said.

"Kusselson! Marshal Tom Kusselson," Tragg thought. "If I killed him, my name would be feared all over the territory."

He watched the Marshal riding along the trail out of town, muffled in a Mexican-style poncho and broad, slouch-brimmed hat.

"Zeb Tragg, the man who killed Kusselson." He could hear the awed voices whispering about him even now. He gazed after the Marshal until he vanished into the distance, and then stationed himself with a view of the trail.

Dusk thickened into night and still he sat, chair tipped back on two legs, leaning against the saloon wall, until at last he saw the dark figure returning. Tragg stood up softly as he recognised the poncho-clad rider approaching. About to step forward into the moonlight, the old fear gripped him again. He couldn't move!

Suddenly a barking dog dashed

across in front of the horse, which reared, pawing the air wildly, and threw its rider off. The Marshal landed badly on his right arm, and stood up, clutching it with his other hand. No-one else was in the street, and Tragg hugged the shadows.

Kusselson led his horse over to his office and went inside. Tragg crept up to the window and with a sense of elation watched through a crack in the shutter as the Marshal bandaged up his badly-sprained and swollen right wrist.

GUNFIGHT!

LATER that night Tragg strutted in through the doors of the "Red House" saloon, ordered drinks all round, and then began bragging about how he would make Kusselson look small and then outshoot him.

A hush fell as the doors swung open to admit the Marshal. He was dressed as before, and he rested a gloved hand on the bar.

"Any trouble, Joe?" he said to the barkeeper.

"Only this famous gunfighter here," the man grinned, jerking his thumb at Tragg. "Though all he's shot off so far is his mouth!"

Tragg stepped out on to the floor. A space rapidly cleared between him and the Marshal. With a new-found confidence he faced the lawman and said hoarsely, "Kusselson, I'm callin' you out. You're a no-good, squint-eyed, washed-up gunman who couldn't hit a buffalo with a cannon at five yards."

The Marshal smiled icily. "Give me your gun, sonny, and then beat it out of town and don't come back."

Tragg spat viciously.

"I'm giving you till the count of three, Marshal, and then I'm gonna draw. If you want to chicken out, do it now."

Marshal Kusselson stepped back a pace or two, nonchalantly threw the loose folds of his poncho over his shoulder, and stood there, arms swinging gently by his side.

Tragg was counting. As he reached three a doubt grew in his mind, a persistent nagging doubt that something was wrong somewhere, but he didn't know what or where. His hand flashed to his gun like lightning. But Kusselson shot him squarely before he could even clear leather.

As he fell dying to the sawdust-covered floor, he saw with fading eyes the Marshal re-holster his gun, and the horror of his mistake crystallised in his brain. Tom Kusselson was left-handed!

The STAR-SPANGLED BANGER

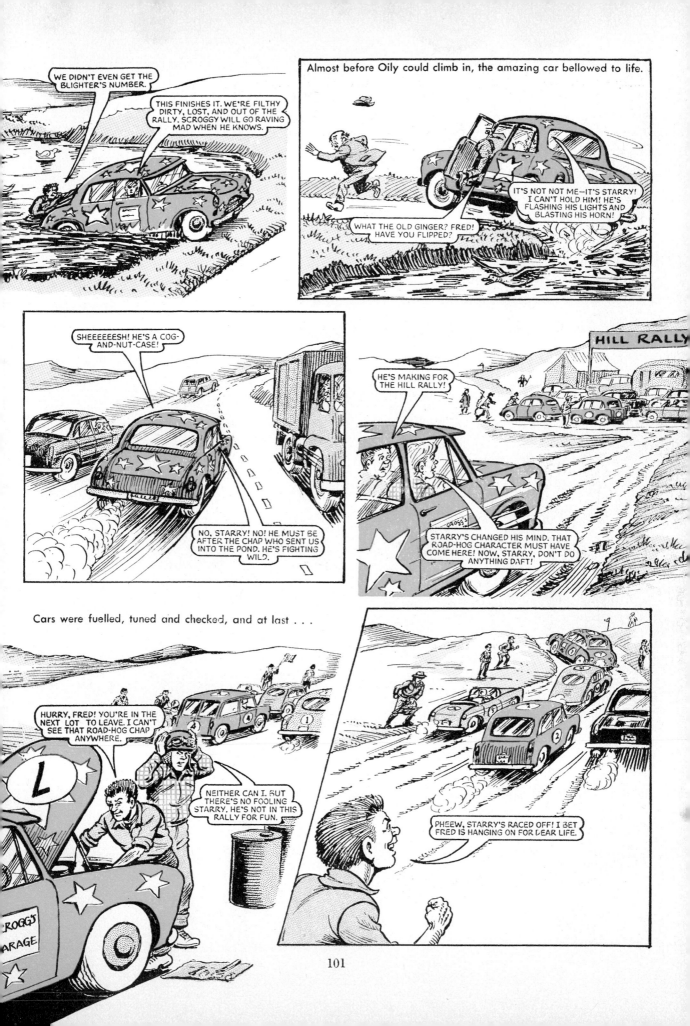

Many entrants were already bogged down . . .   Two circuits later . . .

Mud lay ahead . . .

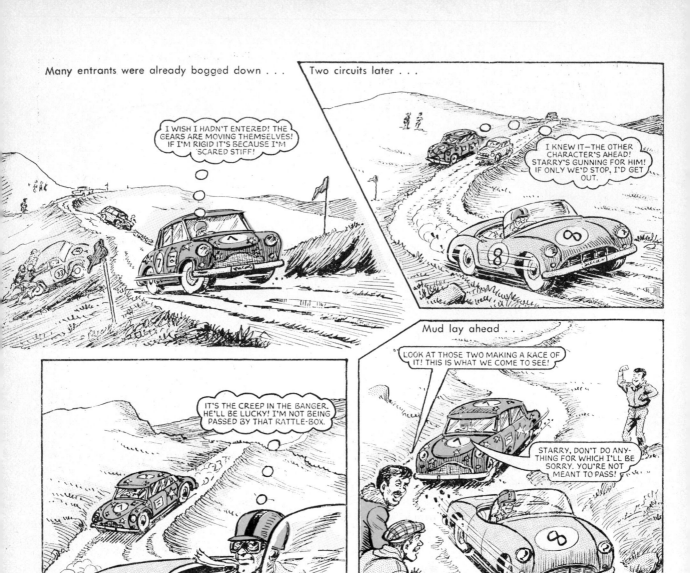

Starry accelerated . . .

An enraged driver climbed from the other car . . .

Starry suddenly rolled forward! . . . .

Later . . .

THE END

FIGARO!

THE O'NEAL SWOOPS IN

THIS BLUSTERING WIND'S CAUSING PROBLEMS AND THAT RISING GROUND'S CAUSING A DOWN-DRAUGHT WHICH COULD DROP ME LIKE A STONE—BUT NOT IF I CAN HELP IT!

Kevin O'Neal, known as "The O'Neal", tried any job that offered excitement. His latest fancy was gliding and he'd built his own plane from scrap. In a gliding contest he'd come third in the distance event and second in the height event. Now he was attempting to put the home-made glider down on a white cross in the centre of the landing ground—where even the experts had failed.

I'M GOING TO MISS THE TARGET BY A MILE. I'LL TRY BANKING QUICKLY.

The O'Neal's glider ran straight into a squall of wind.

THE MAN'S A BEGINNER! THAT SQUALL NEARLY LIFTED THE PLANE ON ITS BACK!

But just as suddenly, the wind disappeared.

BIT O' IRISH LUCK THERE. THE WIND ENDED UP PLAYING RIGHT INTO MY HANDS.

WONDERFUL SKILL! HE'S OUR MAN IF WE CAN GET HIM.

EVERY MAN HAS HIS PRICE!

Later.

COULD YOU LAND ON A SIXPENCE IF THE PRIZE WAS BIG ENOUGH?

PAY ME ENOUGH MONEY, MATE— AND I'LL LAND ON MY NOSE TO PLEASE YOU.

YOU WOULDN'T NEED TO. WE WANT YOU TO LAND IN A SPACE A LITTLE BIGGER THAN A TENNIS COURT AND WE'LL PAY YOU £100,000 TO DO IT. COME, WE MUST TALK.

In their hotel room the two South Americans introduced themselves as Jose Fidano and Manuel Antana.

YOU HAVE HEARD OF US, MY FRIEND?

SURE, YOU'RE PRIME MINISTER IN ORTONA IN SOUTH AMERICA AND YOU, YOU'RE THE CHANCELLOR.

NO LONGER. OUR COUNTRY HAS BEEN TAKEN OVER BY A GANG OF CROOKS LED BY PERO CORTIN. THEY HAVE MADE IT A POLICE STATE RULED BY THE GUN!

OUR PRESIDENT, MATISTE, IS A PRISONER ON MARIO ISLAND. HIS DEATH WAS ANNOUNCED SO THAT THE PEOPLE WOULD LOSE HEART TO FIGHT. MATISTE, A GREAT SCIENTIST, IS WORKING ON INVENTING A NEW METAL, LIGHT AS PLASTIC YET STRONGER THAN STEEL. IT WOULD HAVE MADE THE COUNTRY RICH. ALL THE HOSPITALS AND SCHOOLS WE NEED WOULD HAVE BEEN OURS—BUT CORTIN WANTS THE MONEY FOR HIMSELF.

THE PEOPLE ARE CRUSHED, BUT THERE IS AN UNDERGROUND RESISTANCE GROUP. IF MATISTE WERE TO BE FREED HE COULD LEAD A REVOLT IN PERSON.

ONLY THEN CAN WE HOPE TO DRIVE CORTIN AND HIS CUT-THROATS INTO THE SEA!

Suddenly the runner slipped.

HE'S LOST HIS FOOTING AND GONE OVER THE EDGE! I'LL HAVE TO TRY TO SAVE HIM.

The O'Neal dived in and dragged the man to the side but he was too late.

AS I THOUGHT, ONE OF CORTIN'S HENCHMEN. I'D BETTER GET OUT OF HERE—AND FAST!

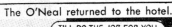

The O'Neal returned to the hotel.

I'LL DO THE JOB FOR YOU. ONE OF CORTIN'S MEN JUST TRIED TO CRUSH ME UNDER TONS OF ROCK! LET'S HEAR YOUR PLAN.

I'M GLAD YOU'VE DECIDED TO JOIN US. THE DEAD MAN MUST HAVE GUESSED WHY WE HAD CONTACTED YOU. CORTIN'S SPIES ARE EVERYWHERE, BUT HE MUST NOT LEARN OF OUR PLAN. WE WILL SETTLE THINGS HERE, THEN MEET AGAIN IN JUYITA, OUR CAPITAL.

They had worked out every detail. No surface craft could slip through the cordon of patrol boats which surrounded Mario Island. A ring of rocket batteries guarded against air attack. In any case, there was no level ground for a plane to land on and a parachute landing was too risky. The plan was for The O'Neal and thirty others to take off from Juyita as an apparently normal charter flight then later transfer to an ex-U.S. Army Horsa glider and head for Mario Island in complete silence.

WE COULD STILL BE PICKED UP ON THE RADAR.

AFTER RELEASING THE GLIDER, THE PLANE WILL TURN IN TOWARDS MARIO, BE PICKED UP ON RADAR AND FIRED UPON. BY THE TIME IT TURNS AWAY AS IF IT HAD STRAYED OFF COURSE THE RADAR WILL BE CONFUSED. THE GLIDER WILL COAST ON TO THE ISLAND IN UTTER SILENCE.

THERE IS A LEDGE OF GRASS-COVERED ROCK ON THE NORTH SIDE OF THE VOLCANIC PEAK. IT IS VERY SMALL BUT A SKILFUL PILOT COULD LAND THERE AT LOW SPEED. WE WILL HAVE MODELS OF THE ISLAND FOR YOU TO STUDY.

IT'S GOING TO BE WORTH EVERY PENNY OF THAT £100,000. WHAT HAPPENS IF WE GET DOWN IN ONE PIECE?

YOU WILL HAVE PLAYED YOUR PART. THE OTHERS WILL CREEP DOWN FROM THE PEAK AND WIPE OUT THE GARRISON WHICH, BECAUSE THEY BELIEVE ATTACK IS IMPOSSIBLE, IS A VERY SMALL ONE. IT WILL BE A SHORT AND BLOODY FIGHT BUT WE WILL HAVE GUNS, EXPLOSIVES AND SURPRISE ON OUR SIDE. FINALLY, WE WILL TURN THE ROCKET BATTERIES ON THE PATROL BOATS.

PRESIDENT MATISTE WILL BROADCAST TO THE MAINLAND. THE PEOPLE WILL KNOW HE IS SAFE AND RISE ALL OVER ORTONA.

TO THE OVERTHROW OF CORTIN, MY FRIENDS.

A week later, The O'Neal arrived in Juyita and awaited contact. One night—

ALL HAS GONE WELL. WE HAVE THE GLIDER HIDDEN ON A DESERTED BEACH FORTY MILES FROM HERE. THE CHARTER PLANE WILL TAKE OFF FROM JUYITA TWO HOURS AFTER NIGHTFALL. IT WILL COLLECT THE GLIDER FROM THE BEACH. AT MIDNIGHT WE SHALL BE OVER MARIO ISLAND.

WE?

I AM GOING TOO! TOMORROW YOU WILL GO TO THIS SHOP AND ASK TO SEE PEDRO. HE WILL SHOW YOU THE WEATHER REPORTS AND A MODEL OF THE ISLAND. WE WILL NOT MEET AGAIN UNTIL THE ATTACK. CORTIN MUST NOT BECOME SUSPICIOUS.

Next day, at Pedro's—

TO LAND AT NORMAL SPEED WOULD BE SUICIDE. I'LL ATTEMPT A STALLED LANDING WITH VERY LITTLE WIND. IT'S RISKY BUT WITH A WIND THERE'D BE A DOWN-DRAUGHT FROM THE MAIN PEAK AND AN UPLIFT BETWEEN THE TWO LOWER PEAKS.

ANY NIGHT WHEN THE WIND IS SOUTH-WEST AND FORCE ONE OR LESS. PASS ON THE MESSAGE, MY FRIEND.

Two nights later, in The O'Neal's hotel.

I CAN RECOMMEND THAT, SENOR.

TONIGHT. CHARTER FLIGHT 14. 20·00 HOURS

I WILL HAVE IT.

And so—

THERE'S THE DAKOTA. EVERYTHING'S GONE SMOOTHLY UP TO NOW. HOPE IT LASTS!

HOPE YOU'VE GOT YOUR FINGERS CROSSED, MATES. WE'RE GONNA NEED ALL THE LUCK WE CAN GET!

WE'RE DOWN!

But The O'Neal, knocked unconscious in the landing, knew nothing of the battle outside.

Shortly.

WHAT HAPPENED?

WE DID IT! ONE MAN WAS KILLED IN THE LANDING. BUT THE WHOLE GARRISON WAS ON THAT SLOPE WHEN WE SWOOPED AND HIT THEM.

THE LANDING WAS A MIRACLE. THAT SLOPE WAS ALMOST VERTICAL. BUT PRESIDENT MATISTE WAS FOUND UNHARMED. HE HAS BROADCAST AND THE REVOLT HAS STARTED. CORTIN IS FINISHED. BUT I ALSO HAVE SOME BAD NEWS.

I DISCOVERED MY FORMULA WAS USELESS JUST AFTER I WAS CAPTURED. I DIDN'T TELL CORTIN—OR HE WOULD HAVE KILLED ME.

SO ORTONA WON'T BE RICH AND YOU CAN'T PAY ME THE £100,000 I WAS PROMISED.

WE PROMISED AND WE WILL PAY. WE WILL RAISE THE TAXES. THE PEOPLE WILL PAY HAPPILY.

FORGET IT. USE YOUR MONEY TO BUILD THE HOSPITALS AND SCHOOLS ORTONA NEEDS. I HAD A SCORE TO SETTLE WITH CORTIN MYSELF. I'M QUITS.

YOU ARE A BRAVE AND A GENEROUS MAN, MISTER O'NEAL.

The O'Neal's bravery and generosity were never forgotten. A massive stone statue dedicated to The O'Neal and the luck of the Irish stands in the capital of Ortona.

THE ONE-MAN WAR OF JOHNNY STARR

Billy Waco and his band of six outlaws had robbed a bank in Wichita and were now being hunted by a posse of men led by U.S. Marshal Burke. But the long, gruelling chase had tired the Waco gang's horses.

LOOKS LIKE THAT FALSE TRAIL WE LAID HAS FOOLED BURKE. THE POSSE AIN'T IN SIGHT.

YEAH, BILLY, BUT IT WON'T TAKE THEM LONG TO FIGURE OUT WHAT WE DONE AND OUR HORSES ARE PLUMB TUCKERED OUT. WE GOTTA GET FRESH ONES.

HEY! WE'RE IN LUCK, BOYS. LOOK OVER THERE—A FOUR HORSE TEAM AND TWO LED HORSES.

GLORY BE! NOW LISTEN, BOYS, THIS IS HOW WE'LL TAKE IT...

Aboard the wagon were Henry Starr and his two sons, George and David.

TAKE IT NICE AND SLOW, GEORGE. WE'RE ONLY ABOUT FOUR DAYS AWAY FROM OKLAHOMA TERRITORY AND THE LAND RUSH AIN'T FOR TEN DAYS.

DON'T WORRY, PAW. OUR HORSES'LL BE GOOD AND FRESH FOR THE RACE AND WE'LL PEG OURSELVES OUT A REAL GOOD SPREAD OF LAND.

IT SURE IS LUCKY FOR US THE GOVERNMENT DECIDED TO ENCOURAGE POPULATING OKLAHOMA BY GRANTING FREE LAND TO THE FIRST TO PEG IT. OUR OLD PLACE IN KANSAS WAS WORKED OUT.

PUT YOUR RIFLE ACROSS YOUR KNEES, PAW. THIS IS A TOUGH-LOOKING OUTFIT THAT'S APPROACHING.

OKAY, SON. DAVID, GET TO THE BACK AND KEEP YOUR EYES SKINNED.

113

But . . .

Not far away, sixteen-year-old Johnny Starr had been hunting for food with his old muzzle loader.

AAH!

GOT HIM!

But McGuire's bullet had only creased Johnny's head.

PAW, GEORGE, DAVID—ALL DEAD. THE MURDERING SKUNKS'LL PAY FOR THIS. I'LL GET THEM IF IT'S THE LAST THING I DO!

Knowing that the posse would eventually see through his false trail ruse, Waco pushed his men on, until . . .

AAH!

THE HOSS BROKE HIS LEG. I'LL HAVE TO SHOOT HIM.

TOO BAD, BILLY. AND YOUR OTHER HOSS IS STILL TIRED.

ALL THE HORSES ARE TIRED. WHAT SAY WE REST UP HERE, BILLY? A LITTLE SHUT-EYE WILL DO US ALL GOOD.

OKAY, BUT I WAS HOPING TO GET NEARER THE MEXICAN BORDER BEFORE HOLING UP FOR THE NIGHT.

THERE'S A CAVE UP HERF I USED TO KNOW, BILLY. WE'LL BE SNUG AS FLEAS IN A BEAR'S SKIN.

GET THE HORSES UNSADDLED! WE'LL STAND FORTY-FIVE MINUTES GUARD EACH AND I'LL DO THE LAST SPELL. THAT WAY I'LL BOOT YOU ALL AWAKE AT DAWN.

Until his family set out for Oklahoma, Johnny Starr had never owned a saddle horse and he was used to walking long distances in search of game for the pot.

He guessed that the men who had stolen the horses must have been riding hard and would rest soon, so he set off after them. He walked all night and shortly after dawn he came upon Waco's dead horse, which he recognised.

Hoof prints showed him which way the gang had gone and there were no return prints. A little earlier, Waco had been roused for his turn on guard . . .

Johnny lay still for about five minutes. Then . . .

A little later . . .

Johnny set off after Waco's gang with the four horses used by the two dead outlaws. By switching horses whenever the one he was riding began to tire, he soon began to overhaul the outlaws. When he was within fifty yards of them, he halted.

But the heavy report of the Henry rifle scared the horse, which reared and threw Johnny to the ground.

THE BARRSIDE THUNDERBOLT

Fourteen-year-old Gordon Davies was on top of the world! The roads around Barrside, the tiny village where he lived had been washed out by three days of incessant rain and he was unable to travel to school in the nearby town of Midchester.

So Gordon paid a visit to the Barrside Tram Museum, where his friend, old Joe, was caretaker . . .

THERE'S NOT MUCH CHANCE OF TAKING OUT A TRAM IN THIS RAIN! IT'S THE HEAVIEST WE'VE HAD FOR YEARS!

YE'RE RIGHT, LAD! THERE WON'T BE MANY VISITORS TODAY.

HEY, JOE! CAN YOU COME DOWN TO HILLSIDE FARM AND LEND A HAND? THE RIVER'S OVERFLOWING AND WE NEED EVERY MAN TO FILL SANDBAGS TO PROTECT THE HOUSE! YOU COME TOO, GORDON.

RIGHT AWAY, CONSTABLE.

JOE, I WANT YOU TO DIG OUT THE SAND TO PUT IN THE SANDBAGS. GORDON CAN HELP ME FILL THEM UP!

At Hillside Farm, Gordon and the others joined the battle against the rising waters . . .

IT'S STILL POURING! I HOPE THIS SANDBAG WALL STOPS THE RIVER BURSTING ITS BANKS!

Suddenly . . .

HEY! SOMEBODY HELP! PART OF THIS MOUNTAIN OF SAND'S COLLAPSED ON OLD JOE!

C'MON, GORDON! LET'S GO!

After several minutes of desperate activity . . .

WELL, WE'VE UNCOVERED HIM, BUT HE'S UNCONSCIOUS—LOOKS BAD! WE'VE GOT TO GET HIM TO HOSPITAL!

BUT WE CAN'T REACH THE HOSPITAL! THE ROAD TO MIDCHESTER IS WASHED OUT!

I'LL CALL UP H.Q. ON MY PERSONAL RADIO AND GET THEM TO SEND A HELICOPTER. IT'S THE ONLY WAY!

A few minutes later . . .

IT'S NO GOOD, LAD! THEY WON'T BE ABLE TO SEND A HELICOPTER FOR HOURS.

THAT'S NO GOOD. OLD JOE'S HURT BAD...WAIT A MINUTE! MAYBE THE ROAD'S WASHED OUT, BUT THE TRAMLINE ISN'T! JOE SHOWED ME HOW TO DRIVE THE TRAMS. I'LL TAKE HIM TO HOSPITAL.

BUT THAT'S IMPOSSIBLE! THE TRAMS HAVEN'T RUN TO MIDCHESTER FOR YEARS! BESIDES, SOME OF THE JOURNEY IS UPHILL AND THERE ARE NO OVERHEAD ELECTRIFIED CABLES.

OH, YES THERE ARE! HALF-A-MILE OF THEM WERE LEFT AS A TOURIST ATTRACTION. IF WE PICK UP ENOUGH SPEED IN THAT HALF-MILE, WE SHOULD HAVE ENOUGH MOMENTUM TO GET OVER THE CREST OF THE HILL. THEN IT'S DOWNHILL ALL THE WAY TO MIDCHESTER.

Back at the museum . . .

I'LL TAKE THAT ONE! IT'S HEAVIER THAN A SINGLE-DECKER AND SHOULD BE MORE STABLE ON THE OLD TRACK!

RIGHT, SON, IT'S ALL UP TO YOU. I'LL SWITCH ON THE POWER AND YOU CAN TAKE IT OUT OF THE SHED.

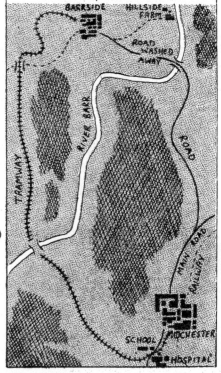

Gordon was right. It was possible to take a tram to Midchester. Once over the small hill outside Barrside, the tram could freewheel all the way—but on such a day it was a perilous venture!

I'VE PHONED MIDCHESTER HOSPITAL AND TOLD THEM WHAT WE'RE DOING. THEY'LL HAVE AN AMBULANCE WAITING FOR US AT THE END OF THE LINE.

RIGHT, CONSTABLE BURTON. HOP ABOARD, THEN, AND KEEP YOUR FINGERS CROSSED!

Gordon pressed the starter and the old tram leapt into life.

WE'VE GOT TO PICK UP ENOUGH SPEED TO GET US OVER THE CREST OF THE HILL!

AND WE'VE ONLY GOT HALF-A-MILE OF ELECTRIFIED TRACK TO DO IT IN! BUT WE'LL DO IT—NOTHING'LL STOP THE BARRSIDE THUNDERBOLT!

WE'VE LEFT THE OVERHEAD CABLES, BUT HAVE WE ENOUGH SPEED TO GET US OVER THE HILL?

WE'RE SLOWING UP! IT'LL BE TOUCH AND GO!

WE'VE MADE IT! NEXT STOP MIDCHESTER!

But . . .

BLIMEY! THE TRAMLINE BRIDGE IS DOWN AND WE'RE GOING TOO FAST TO STOP!

THE RAILS ARE STILL INTACT THOUGH! WE'LL HAVE TO GIVE IT A TRY!

BRING UP THE TROOPS!

All these vehicles were used for transporting soldiers and their equipment during the Second World War.

FORD GPW (JEEP) TRUCK (AMERICAN)

BUFFALO LANDING CRAFT (ALLIED)

BMW R75 MOTOR-CYCLE COMBINATION (GERMAN)

SD. KFZ-251/7 PERSONNEL CARRIER (GERMAN)